Barrelhouse

fiction.
poetry.
pop flotsam.
cultural jetsam.

issue four
new fiction, poetry, essays, interviews, and stuff

issn 1555-7227

editorial

fiction editors
Dave Housley
Mike Ingram
Joe Killiany
Matt Kirkpatrick
Aaron Pease

poetry editors
Dan Brady
Gwydion Suilebhan

copy editor
Ilana Boivie

art director
Kylos Brannon

cover
art by Mike Fitts
design by Kylos Brannon

board of directors
Dan Brady
Megan Farrell
Danielle Natoli
Thisbe Nissen
Homer Wieder

Barrelhouse owes a special thank you to
Stephen R. Rourke, Esq., of Rourke & Rosenberg, LLC,
as well as Maryland Lawyers for the Arts.

Printed by Signature Book

For information about ordering, subscribing, or submitting to Barrelhouse, or to option Barrelhouse and the life stories of its editors for a Hollywood blockbuster or prime time soap opera:

visit our website at: www.barrelhousemag.com
or send an email to: webmaster@barrelhousemag.com

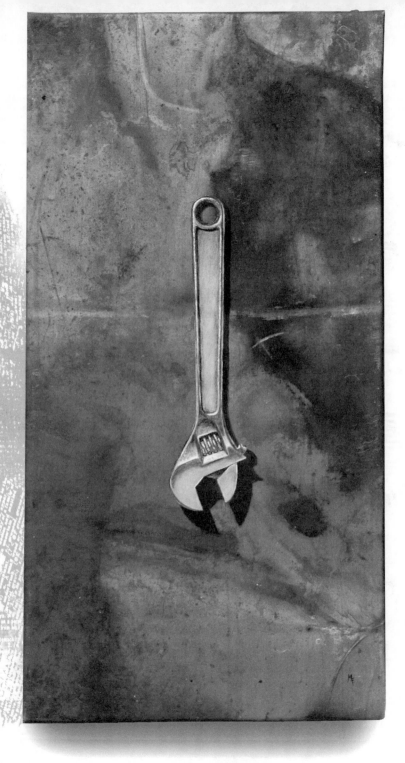

art by Mike Fitts

TABLE OF CONTENTS

FICTION

The Bed   by Paul Maliszewski   ...1

Walls   by Tod Goldberg   ...8

Performance Reviews from No Man's Land
    by Mark Peebles Brown   ...23

Mario's Three Lives   by Matt Bell   ...61

MeChip   by David Barringer   ...69

For Frankie   by Paul Maliszewski   ...115

ESSAYS

The Great Escape   by Pete MacDonald   ...47

For the Love of Good TV   by Melanie Springer Mock   ...95

INTERVIEWS

Malcolm Gladwell   ...33

the Hold Steady   ...81

Paul Soter of Broken Lizard   ...106

THE ILLUSTRATED STORY

Baldy   written by Joe Killiany   ...126
adapted and illustrated by Gordon McAlpin

POETRY

How I Came to Write This Poem   by Joan Colby   ...17

The Great Depression   by Joan Colby   ...20

Land of Dead Babies   by Rebecca Cook   ...28

Aubade with a Quincy Jones Biography on PBS   by Barbara Duffey ...30

Sometimes Women Have Greater Portions of Learning Than Wis-
dom Which is No Better Use to Them Than a Maynsale to a Fly Boat
by Eva Hooker   ...43

When I Ask My Friend Susan Why She Doesn't Like Oatmeal,

She Tells Me This Story   by Amorak Huey   ...44

Jerry Seinfeld's Favorite Poem   by Wendy Babiak   ...56

Doc Holliday on the Importance of Comradeship:
Tombstone, Arizona, October 25, 1881   by Jennifer L. Knox   ...58

At Noon Through the Binoculars   by Jennifer L. Knox   ...59

Returning   by Sandra Kohler   ...64

The Flat Land   by Kate Lovelady   ...66

Our Love Poems Are in Janis Joplin's Stockpot   by Allison McEntire ...92

In Memory of a Book   by Valzhyna Mort   ...100

Utopia   by Valzhyna Mort   ...102

Ambien   by Sarah Sloat   ...122

The Gaze   by Gary J. Whitehead   ...124

 DEAR

Have you ever been to a rock and roll concert? We're not talking about that time you hung out at a warehouse in Brooklyn while some shaggy-haired hipster moped through a few dirges about how hard it is to get laid. Nor are we talking about that time sophomore year when the hippyish girl down the hall played a couple of acoustic sets at the coffeehouse and it was all so beautiful and tragic that you wondered, just briefly, what it might feel like to stick your tongue into another woman's mouth. No, dear reader, what we're talking about here is a True Rock and Roll Experience, the kind of thing that can only happen in a poorly ventilated arena, with wailing guitar solos and questionable haircuts and ditchweed smoked through an apple. If there's a keytar and a fog machine, so much the better.

Have you ever been to a show like that?

We hope, for your sake, that you have. The band's just ripped through its first two numbers - a couple of the radio hits, though not The Big Radio Hit - and they spend maybe half a minute chatting up the crowd. They say something like: "How's everybody feeling tonight?" Or: "Are you ready to rock?" Or: "So we were driving down Highway 90/Route 10/Alfalfa Boulevard today, and this town sure does have a lot of lot of hockey fans/random tire fires/saltwater taffy."

This 30 or 60 or 90 seconds of meaningless chit chat has a name, dear reader, and that name is Banter. Banter is a staple of the True Rock Experience, and while you've probably never given it a second thought, we'd like for you to think about it right now, if only for a couple of minutes.

Why, you ask?

Reason #1: What you're reading right now, these words and these paragraphs and this entire trying-hard-to-be-charming letter, is one hundred percent Banter.

Reason #2: Banter is basically bullshit.

Look: when some rock and roller comes out on stage and starts chatting you up, what he wants you to think is: "I'm feeling pretty good, thanks to you, plus those thirteen Natty Lights I shotgunned in the lot." Or:

READER

"As a matter of fact, I *would* like to rock." Or: "We *do* have a lot of tire fires." And then you let your guard down. *These rock and rollers aren't such bad people,* you think; *in fact, they actually kind of get where I'm coming from.*

The point is this, dear reader: A True Rock Experience is not about some corny Banter. The reason we yearn to Rock - the only reason - is that we want - nay, *desperately need* - ten thousand watts of pure rock power blasted into our brains. Likewise, you shouldn't buy a literary journal - say, this literary journal - because the editors wrote a charming little letter and they seem like perfectly nice guys who are probably harmless with their glasses and messenger bags and thrift-store hoodies. The only reason to buy a literary journal - say, this literary journal - is because you want - nay, *desperately need* - ten thousand watts of pure literary power blasted into that space just below your sternum that in less ironic times we referred to as The Soul.

So consider the Banter, dear reader, and then discard it. Stay, instead, for the Pure Literary Power: for Paul Maliszewski's alter ego pouring out his heart and soul to the President (twice!), for Tod Goldberg's funny yet totally heartbreaking rendering of a typical American family, for Mark Peebles Brown's weird world of cubicle warfare, for Matt Bell's weird world of Mario and for Dave Barringer's weird ... well, just weird, weird world. Stay for the poems, dear reader, for the insightful and soul-baring interviews (three of them! in one single issue!), stay for the essays on popcorn movies and our collective love of television.

Those rock stars, dear reader, are not real people. They are not your friends. They are demi-gods, and they deserve your admiration, yes, but also your fear. And the five of us? The dudes who with loving kindness have delivered to you this fourth installment of Barrelhouse in all its literary glory? We, dear reader, we are your Overlords.

Rock on, Dear Reader. And keep on barrelhousing, all night long.

Dave, Joe, Mike, Aaron and Matt

THE BED

by
Paul Maliszewski

RETURN TO SENDER
212
Insufficent Address

LEBANON,
JUL 20
6-PM
1962
PA.

U.S. POSTAGE
00.29 3
H METER 80497

April 15, 2002
Dear President Bush,

A few nights ago I became superstitious about my bed. After several nights of lying awake, starting at every sound and getting up to check the windows and door to see that they were locked, I decided that the best thing to do was to blame the bed for my problems, pull a blanket onto the floor, and sleep there. The bed is, so you understand, the one in which Nancy and I formerly slept.

Two days of sleeping on the floor was enough to convince me to see about the purchase of a new bed. And calling around to a few bed places was enough to convince me that I could not at this time afford the purchase of most new beds.

But I prevailed, sir, and found a place with an inexpensive bed. A kind woman on the phone told me what she had was as good as a bed. I was sold.

I asked, "How soon can you deliver?" In my mind I was already sleeping on my bed. Nobody had slept on it before me. I was relaxing on my bed, eating meals in front of the television, and then falling asleep in my clothes.

The woman said, "Oh, we don't deliver, dear."

I said, "You don't." I said it like a statement but meant it like a question.

The woman said, "No, we never deliver. That's how we keep our prices lower than the competition."

An hour later Ted was driving me to pick up the new bed.

"Never heard of a bed place that won't deliver beds," Ted said.

"The lady said it had to do with keeping their prices low," I said.

"I'll bet," Ted said.

"What's that supposed to mean?"

"It means," Ted said, "I'll bet it has to do with any number of things other than keeping their prices low."

"Whatever," I said.

"For example," Ted said. He looked over at me, expecting me to, I guess, interrupt or cut him off.

I didn't say anything.

"For example," Ted said, "suppose they used to deliver beds, but one of their bed-delivery persons got in an accident while delivering them. Maybe he was reckless. Or maybe he was drinking. He was probably drunk while delivering the beds, and that's why he caused the accident, one in which an innocent family died. The family had two girls, a loving mother, and a supportive father. The mother and the father were upstanding members of their community and active in their church. They were professionals of some sort or other. The girls were beautiful. They were just beautiful American girls, you know, and the newspapers and the television stations showed their beautiful pictures every chance they could. The whole family wore nice clothes in all their pictures. You could tell they were nice clothes just by looking at them. The bed-delivery person, on the other hand, in all his pictures he was unshaven. Also, one of his eyelids looked droopy, and his eyes were glassy. Anyway, the bed company had what anyone would call a public outcry type situation on its hands, and so the president had to come out and say, 'I will not deliver any more beds until I personally get to the bottom of this tragic debacle.' He used the phrase 'tragic debacle' whenever he addressed what happened or talked to reporters. He was all 'This tragic debacle should never have happened' and 'I will not rest until this tragic debacle receives the closure it deserves.' He said 'tragic debacle' so many times, in fact, that people started to pick up on it, as people will, you know. People started describing things that weren't remotely like tragic debacles as tragic debacles."

"You finished?" I asked.

Ted said, "Harvey, that driver was guilty of recklessly endangering an innocent family."

"First of all," I said, "you don't know anything about any driver. Second of all, that's not a crime."

"Recklessly endangering is a crime," Ted said. "It very much is a crime."

"Right," I said, "but they don't call it 'recklessly endangering an innocent family.'" I made the first two fingers of my hands into quotation marks and hooked them around his words as if I didn't dare touch them with my entire hands.

Ted fell silent. A vein pulsed in his neck. He drove a couple of miles. "You don't know that for sure," he said.

That evening Ted and I set up my new bed—really more of a futon, technically speaking—and then carried the old bed down to the curb.

"Seems like there should be some kind of ceremony for this," Ted said.

I stood looking at the bed. The mattress was leaning against a row of mailboxes. Seams that had long ago started to give were now opened up fully, exposing the innards. The box-spring lay half on the grass and half flattening out a bed of tall weeds that had completely overtaken something else, I don't know what. And the frame was split into two parts, both twisted back like arms badly broken.

"You okay?" Ted said.

"Yes," I said, "just looking at this bed."

Ted looked at me as if to say no shit you're just looking at this bed.

"I'm thinking," I said. "I said I was looking at the bed, but what I meant to say was that I was thinking."

Ted said, "We could invent some ritual if you want."

"I don't know," I said.

"Fire's always good," Ted said.

"I don't have the energy to burn anything," I said.

Ted sat down on the curb, took out a pack of cigarettes and struck it against the palm of his hand a few times. Then he started fiddling with the plastic wrapper.

"You got a bed on the side of the road, a bed that looks fairly good, fairly sturdy, you just know something went wrong inside and, probably, somebody couldn't sleep and you better believe you can guess why that person couldn't sleep."

"Beds just look all wrong when they're out of the bedroom," I said.

"Stands to reason," Ted said.

"No," I said. "I mean, look at it. A few minutes ago, when it was inside, when it had my sheets and pillows on it, it looked like something. It was something. It was a piece of my home, you know?"

Ted lit up and nodded his head as if he understood.

"Now it looks like the scene of some—"

"Tragic debacle?"

"It looks like something right and good and stable has been overturned and upset and fucked with. And everybody who drives by knows it, too. You got a bed on the side of the road, a bed that looks fairly good, fairly sturdy, you just know something went wrong inside and, probably, somebody couldn't sleep and you better believe you can guess why that person couldn't sleep."

Ted looked up at me. "That's a lot to get out of one bed," Ted said. "These people who know everything, are they driving by real slow?"

"I saw a car being towed away the other night," I said. "Perfectly good car. Looked new, you know. But there was something about seeing that car tilted up at an angle and going backwards that made me think I was witnessing evidence of some specific human sadness. I shouldn't have seen it, but I did."

"Cars get towed every day," Ted said. "I see them all the time."

"Or, say, for example that you come home and find your neighbor locked out of his apartment and getting sick on his doorstep."

"I'm not sure I follow you," Ted said.

I felt full of confusion and betrayed by my own tongue. "It's like this," I said, starting again. "It's like if I saw that car that was being towed instead just on the ground, flat, at no angle, and headed in the right direction, I wouldn't have thought twice about it. I wouldn't have wondered about the owner's life or anything. No sadness there. No reason to look for any sadness, right?"

Ted shrugged.

"And if," I said, "my bed were assembled, if we, if you and I, put it back together, if we did that right now, people driving by wouldn't even know something wrong happened here."

"We can put the bed together," said Ted. "That's not a problem. It'll only take five minutes."

"I just feel like I got my disappointments and shortcomings stacked on the curb," I said. I walked over to the mattress. "They're all just here to be read," I said. I ran my right hand across the top of the mattress, moving it from left to right. The surface was bumpy and marked elsewhere by slight discolorations, some rough spots, and a few patches worn smooth. "I disappointed Nancy," I said. My hand slid to the right as I talked then came down an inch and back over to the left again. "I disappointed Abby and Nick. I made enormous mistakes, and now my bed is on the curb for anybody to see."

Ted took a drag on his cigarette, placed it gingerly on the ground and then ran his fingers through his hair. "People might think you just bought a new bed," he said. "You know, something better."

"It's all in the angle," I said. "Beds just look all wrong when they're out of the bedroom."

The sun was down almost when, a few minutes later, I started putting the frame together, but while the light was fading fast, I had the bed completely assembled before dusk shaded into nightfall.

Ted got up to take a look at my handiwork. "Those mailboxes make an attractive nightstand," he said. "And those weeds are quite a stunning headboard."

"At least it looks like a bed again," I said. I sat down on the mattress and looked up and down the street. No cars. Ted sat down beside me. A girl went by on a bicycle. Her brother ran by a few seconds later, screaming at her, saying she was going to be in some trouble. Ted finished his cigarette and put it out on the curb. He stepped on it, taking his time, and then made ready to leave. I thanked him for his help, saying what I always say, which is that there's no way I can ever repay him. Ted said what he always says, which is that there's no way I will ever need to repay him.

After Ted left I waited on the bed until well after dark. A few fireflies emerged from the thicket across the street. One flicked on. In response, another, just a few feet away, flicked on. Then a third flicked on then off and then on again.

Keep up the good work, sir.

Sincerely,

Harvey Strub

ROCK POSTER SKETCHES

by Jay Ryan of the Bird Machine
www.thebirdmachine.com

WALLS

BY TOD GOLDBERG

art by Cecelia Ferriera

We were not consulted. It was the 1970s. And then it was the early 1980s. What would happen is that they would come to the door, smelling of Brute, or smelling of cigarettes and the fine leather interior of their Grand Torinos or TR-7s, and they would say, "I'm here to pick up Sally. This the right house?"

We'd say, "Yeah, come on in. She's getting dressed." Or we'd say, "Do you mean Mommy?" Or, and this was rare, but it happened because we were young and angry and when your parents have divorced and all you have to show for it is a mother who has suddenly decided that she'd like to fuck as many men as possible, and a father who it turns out was gay, but you wouldn't know that until long after he was dead and you found the photos and the letters, but who, at the time, was dating a woman named Ms. Lisa who hosted *Romper Room* on Channel 2, we'd say: "Are you our new daddy?" It was cruel, but we were smart and we were sad and we had agendas.

We kept a list. We updated it nightly. We remember you. That's what this is all about. We remember you. We thought you'd stay. We thought, on the day before the last night, when you sat us down and said that you'd stay but that our mother was crazy, was ruining your life, was ruining our lives, too, and if you had any legal rights, why, you'd take us out of this house. You told us you'd just wait until our mother went to work and you'd back up a big truck and we'd all just move our stuff into it: We'd take the two dogs, Sam and Roxanne, and we'd pull up the yellow shag carpet in the family room, the hundreds of Star Wars action figures, the posters of Peter Frampton, the posters of Rick Springfield, the posters of Heather Thomas, the EZ-Bake Oven, the Risk board, the photo albums from when we still had the beach house, back when Mom still looked so young, still had that Jackie O thing going for her. Dad used to be in those photos too, but he's gone, cut out, just a shoulder or a foot or the brim of a hat barely visible in a jagged corner.

You were a cop, we remember that. But then you quit your job after you saw a guy get his head blown off. BLAM, you said. BLAM and then there was nothing but a stump. You said that's what made you quit your job and become a steel worker and then you lost that job because people had a way of dying around you. People had a way of being near you and then not being near you. They said you didn't follow protocol. That you were responsible for an industrial accident. And so you lived in our house for a little while and that was good. We felt so calm. We felt normal. We felt the wall shake when you had sex with our mother, but that was okay, because you were good. And we felt the wall shake when you'd climb into her shower and sob, banging your fists against the tile, probably unaware that her bathroom backed up to one of our bedrooms.

We remember you.

We remember Doug Loomis. He called accidentally, looking for someone else, but Mom liked his voice, told him she thought he sounded very interesting, wondered if he might like to buy her a drink the next time he was in town. She called him "Wrong Number" and she told us he had a boat and that he really wanted to take us all out on it, that we'd sail to Catalina, or Hawaii, or Peru, and that he loved all of us kids. Doug Loomis was bald. Doug Loomis showed up in our kitchen one Sunday morning and asked us to make him some coffee. Asked us to get him the newspaper. Asked us if we could quiet the fuck down. Mom wanted to know, a few days later, what we'd done to "Wrong Number" because he no longer called, not even by accident.

You once took us to a park and told us to forget who our parents were. You told us to pretend that you were our father and that the woman who'd just thrown a platter of frozen meat at us was a burglar.

We remember Cy Cohen. Cy Cohen sold Seiko watches. In the morning, he'd walk outside in one of our father's old bathrobes and he'd read the paper standing up on the driveway. Cy Cohen drove an Alfa Romeo. Cy Cohen used to scream his own name at night. It sounded like this: "Oh, fuck yes, Cy!" Cy Cohen lasted a few weeks, actually, long enough to enjoy Thanksgiving in our home. He gave us all Seiko watches. He left them on doilies next to our plates. They were thick and silver. They glowed in the dark. They pulled our wrists down. They kept imperfect time. Mom told us Cy cared very deeply for us, would probably want to adopt us, that he loved us very much. We wrote excessively long thank you notes to Cy for the watches. A week after Cy Cohen stopped his eponymous joy, he showed up at the house and demanded all of our watches back.

You told us we'd be eighteen one day. You told us to hold onto that.

We remember Mark Simon. Mark had three kids, all boys, and they were big scary fucks. They went to school with us. They used to beat the shit out of us. They once tied us to the bike racks in front of Castle Rock Elementary and threw walnuts at our genitals. They said things like, "We're going to make your pussies bleed." Mark Simon owned a chain of hardware stores. He wore golf shirts with a penguin logo. He had silver hair that he kept cut short, like he was in the military. Mark Simon starred in his own commercials where he'd say, "Hi, kids! I'm Mark Simon. Go get your parents and tell them I'm on TV and want to make a deal with them!" Mom met Mark Simon when she was thinking about becoming a realtor. She went to some community mixer where he was the toastmaster. She didn't come home for two days, just left a message on the Record-A-Call that said she'd met someone, that we should eat the Swanson Chicken TV dinners in the freezer, that we should ask Stephanie Howser's mom to drive us to school. The three Simon boys cornered us at school and told us that our mother sounded like a malfunctioning back hoe when she was getting fucked, that she made shitty pancakes and that if we weren't careful, they'd make our pussies bleed.

Your sister died while you were living in our house. We went to the funeral even though we didn't know her. It was December, a few days before Christmas, and the service was held out in Benicia. In the distance, we could see the Navy Mothball Fleet docked out in the shallow bay. You got up during the service and you said that you were sorry that you'd been such a terrible brother to her, that you'd let her make so many mistakes, that you should have just picked her up in your arms and carried her away, put her in a place where she could get the help she needed, where she wouldn't find a way to meet guys like you, Freddie, you fucking cocksucker. You made eye contact with us. We nodded our heads and mouthed that we loved you. We went to Farrell's afterward and ate hot fudge sundaes. You told us stories about your sister. You told us she lived in regret. You told us her negativity propelled her towards drugs and guys like Freddie who would rather kick her fucking ass than kiss her on the lips. When Mom said not to use such language in front of us, you said, "You remind me of her a lot, Sally. You really do. That's not a compliment."

We remember Jack Morken. Jack wore velour. Jack went to Purdue on a basketball scholarship in some nebulous, yellowed past, but that didn't stop him from wearing Purdue sweatshirts and Purdue t-shirts and velour pullover v-neck sweaters with a tiny Purdue logo stitched over the chest. Jack Morken owned a limo service and said he had a house up in Tahoe. Every time he came to pick up Mom, a long, black limo would pull up in front of our house. "Jack's here," we'd say, watching him through the living room window, his shadow barely visible as he slid through the opening between the front seat and the back seat so he could get out through the back passenger door. The neighbors would come out onto their front porches to see who was in the limo, because this was in the 1970s and not just anyone could get a limo, unless you had $75 to spend for the evening. We got to drive in the limo once. It was raining and we pounded on the master bedroom door to let Mom know we needed a ride to school, that all of us would be drenched if we walked, that there was lightning that might kill us. Jack came to the door. "Your mom says to ask the neighbors for a ride," Jack said, "but why don't I take you?" We climbed into the back of the limo and it was nothing like we imagined. The seats were once crushed red velvet, but now they were crusted and hard, black electrical tape keeping them together in places. It smelled of perfume and cigars and something like vinegar, but more pungent. We found a bra on the floor. We found a high-heeled shoe. We found Marlboro butts in the ashtray. We found handprints on the back window. We found Jack staring at us through the dividing window at the stop sign on the corner of our street. It looked like he wanted to cry, or he wanted to cough, or he wanted this moment in his life to end, because he just kept staring at us before finally saying, "I'm sorry. You guys should just walk."

You took us for lobster on the day your unemployment ran out.

We remember Dan Kern. Dan was our stepfather for six months. Dan was a lawyer. Dan spoke German fluently. Dan wore bikini underwear long before it was fashionable. Dan had three children from a previous marriage, though all of them were adopted. Steven, Bonnie, and Lyle came to live with us on weekends, sharing our rooms, eating our

Pop-Tarts, changing the TV from reruns of *The Monkees* to reruns of *Get Smart* without even asking. Dan didn't particularly care for the fact that we didn't call him Dad. He asked us if we loved him. We said no. He asked us why not. We told him we didn't even know him. Mom told us he was going to adopt us and we were going to change our last names and that Dan was going to get full custody of his kids and we'd all live together in a big house in Pacific Heights. Then Steven beat up his grandma with a broom stick and told everyone that Johnny Carson told him to do it. Then Bonnie brought a Ouija board to our house and started taking her top off around us, which caused problems, because we weren't related and we were young and we knew from the shaking wall that there was possibility in all of this, that we could all scream our names and no one would know what it meant but us. Then Lyle showed up at homecoming dressed as a woman and we found out that he had the machinery to be both and he'd made a choice, because he was sixteen, and he was now Linda. One day shortly thereafter, Dan chased us all into the garage. He was wearing his Hawaiian print bikini underwear and was waving around a butcher knife and screamed at us in German. And then he wasn't our stepfather anymore.

He asked us if we loved him. We said no. He asked us why not. We told him we didn't even know him.

You showed up at our graduations. We saw you in the back. It had been years, but we recognized you. We looked for you afterwards and since we never found you, we began to think that maybe you weren't really there, were just a mirage, just us wishing you'd reappear.

We remember when there was no one left. We remember when the men stopped coming because Mom had become sick, was told she'd be dead in six months, though of course she never did die. But by then we were gone. We came back as adults to care for her, back to our old bedrooms. We slept on our Star Wars sheets. We listened to The Knack and Gordon Lightfoot and Journey and REO Speedwagon and The Thompson Twins and Shaun Cassidy and Blondie and talked about how much those songs used to mean to us, so much so that when Mom would scream "Down or off!" we'd just turn it up and wait for the rage, wait for her to walk outside and turn off the power, leaving us in the dark, spinning the records on our old Fisher-Price record players, the music just tinny scratches of sound, a departure from the yelling that rippled down the hallway, that caused Sam and Roxanne, the dogs, to crap themselves right where they stood. We found Bonnie's Ouija board and tried to find you there, in case you were dead. We stood Mom up in her shower and bathed her, the water glancing off the tile wall and pooling at our feet and we imagined you standing there alone, hitting that wall, pounding that wall, sobbing, and we reached out to you in our minds in case you stood there still, haunting the shower, your demons buried in the grout along with bits of skin from your knuckles. We put Mom into her bed and it seemed so much smaller than we imagined it. Just a bed. Four corners. Sheets. A headboard. We imagined you there beside her. We tried to figure out what drove you there in the first place. How old were you? 35? 40? Our age now. We have our own beds. We have our own master bedrooms and yet we think of you still, standing here, saying goodbye to her in bed, because that's where it happened. You stood in the doorway of the master bedroom, and you said, "I just can't do this. How many others, Sally? How many?" And she said a number like five or seven or who fucking cares just get the fuck out you no-job-son-of-a-bitch. And you walked down the hallway and poked your head into each of our rooms and you said goodbye and you said sorry and you said you tried for us but that there's a limit and you'd found yours and then the stapler hit you in the back and we looked and Mom was throwing things from her bedroom at you. You just kept walking. You even stopped and hugged the dogs. You put your nose in that space be-tween Sam's eyes and you held her ears and you whispered something. And you picked up Roxanne, who was a collie, and you hugged her like a child and she licked your face. A bottle of your cologne came sailing down through the air and it cracked on the wall and you didn't even move. The hallway still smells of you. Mom would have us shampoo the carpet and scrub the wallpaper but nothing removed the smell. Here we are, decades in the dust, and we find tiny bits of glass still wedged into the wall.

You exist on the Internet. There are one hundred twenty of you in thirty-three different states. We have your numbers. One day we will call. We've mapquested your addresses. One day we will fly to you in

Florida and Iowa and Alaska and Washington and we will knock on your door and when you open it we will say, "Hello, do you remember us?" And you will say no and you will say no and you will say no and then maybe you will say yes, because it will be you and not just a man with your name. You'll be older, too, because there isn't a way for memory to freeze the body like it freezes trauma in place.

Or we will let you be. We will give you that grace. We will drive by your homes across the country and we will imagine you inside and we will wonder if you've known all along that we remember you.

ROCK POSTER SKETCHES

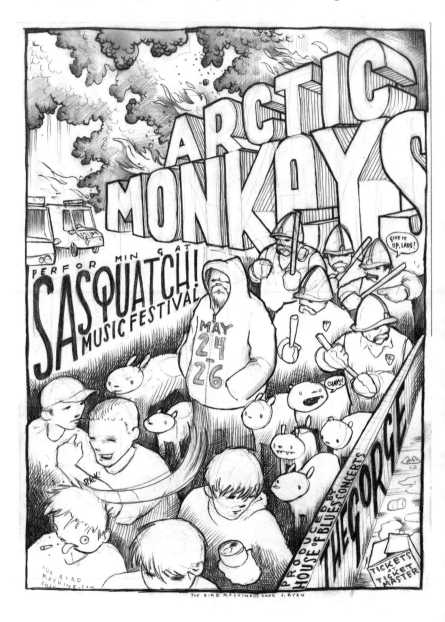

by Jay Ryan of the Bird Machine
www.thebirdmachine.com

How I Came to Write This Poem

by Joan Colby

First, set pieces
Clever as zircons,
Then weather,
A sky of cawing birds
And roiling clouds, my
Metaphor or badlands
Deceivingly pink and gold in dawnlight.

It is the angle of sun
Which captivates,
The molten canyon driving west
At sunset. The pearly morning
Centered with a redbird
Uttering his distinctive query
From the low bush beyond the south window.

The rimrocks hovering like
Ogre nursemaids
Massive, flat-topped
While the town below darkens
And sparkles.
A leaf is an anthem
Everything stands for something,
We paddle still waters
Making a silver groove ·
From which our existence
Like waterbirds perpetually slides forward.

A ring of firs. Black rock.
And always
The dream of white-eyed horses.

When you died, the voices chorused
Like migrating redwings
Filling the bare March trees
With amazing noise, then silence.

I could not open your book,
Examine the photograph or look
At the slanted signature
Of your love. I could not
Feel.

Poetry repulsed me,
Its bleeding scab. Streaking windows
Of rain. Gravel embedded
In mudslick. Why
Write or sing or draw or think,
As Auden said *it changes*
Nothing.

Last spring the rivers rose
Out of their banks in a hundred-year flood.
A terrified boy was swept away
As the news cameras followed. Men
Lowered ropes, attempting to grasp
An extremity as he boiled past
In the deluge crying out.

This boy, a stranger, breaks
My heart. I wept for him
As I never could for you or myself.
Today, the poem says
I will be spoken the way buds clench
Then burst in the false precursor flower.

The true leaf unfurls its nature
Its delicate ribs, fabric tough
And strange, greenskinned,
Thinskinned, willing to suffer
Loss with the wind. All over earth
Turning to powder, the least of us
Essential and here and now.

The Great Depression

by Joan Colby

Stuck to the roofs of their mouths
Like peanut butter.
Afterwards, they could never
Order steak without
Having to carve it into the smallest
Morsels. Dull knives and
Chipped china. They nibbled
Liverwurst sandwiches at their desks
And mended the sheets, and bought
One good suit and simonized
The car until it gleamed
Like money. Money
My god how its lack scarred their faces
Folded into lines like George Washington's
Steely eyed, legal tender, a note
Of federal reserve. They trusted
In God and went hungry, jobless,
Foreclosed, nine people in the house
And not one working.

In the prosperity of 1950
My mother fed the dog bread crusts,
His stools were white and dry.
Let down hems, let out seams, turned
Cuffs and collars, kept
A black book of every spent penny.

Years later, on a cruise, they worried
It was costing a lot, was it worth it?
Each foggy day tormented them,
A purchased view, wasted
and would they get into Glacier Bay?
It wasn't guaranteed, nothing
Was guaranteed.

You can't have the bypass, she
Said. White and ill, he stared at her.
We can't afford it.
What they knew was this:
Everything cherished can be suddenly taken away.

Just like that, he died.
She bargained with the funeral director.
What kind of discount
Was he prepared to give?

Each day, she studies the stock market
In the paper. This is where it starts.
She recites the multiplication tables
When she can't sleep—it will keep
Her mind sharp. There's all those
Sharks out there waiting to take you.
Their shadows hover beyond
The dead-bolt locks.

Setting the thermostat five degrees lower,
Putting on an extra sweater, she remembers
People lost everything

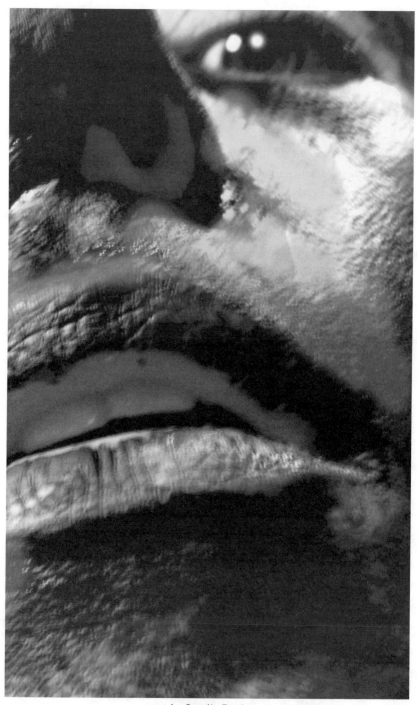

art by Cecelia Ferriera

Barrelhouse

PERFORMANCE REVIEWS FROM NO MAN'S LAND
BY MARK PEEBLES BROWN

At night they broadcast commercials. Actually, I don't know for sure it is them, it could be us. Anyway, somebody broadcasts them, the same ones over and over again. Those disembodied, saccharine-sweet voices and snappy jingles echo out over the smoldering bomb craters of No Man's Land. At night distraction is king. Matt Silk and I talk and play Mattel football with the sound muted to take our minds off the commercials. Silk is struggling; he's having trouble at home. One of his kids has Down Syndrome and his wife blames him for not being around. She thinks he's at a sales conference. She thinks he's entertaining clients at Hooters. He thinks she's sleeping with everyone.

Presentation binders flap through the air over our heads. Outgoing. The shelling is in support of our attack. We are doing a flanking maneuver; we always do a flanking maneuver.

They know it's coming and we take heavy casualties. Jones from Shipping. Tom Slavin. I remember he had a sign on his cubicle, in the days when we had cubicles: *What part of 'No' don't you understand?* The whistles call retreat, and I leave Slavin, pretend I don't see him. He's grossly overweight and will slow me down.

Later, I worm through the labyrinth of trenches and bunkers looking for Ed and Willie. I hunker down and slosh through the mud, not
caring that my suit, Hickey Freeman, is getting ruined at the cuffs. I
find Little Willie sitting on a sandbag, kicking his legs like a schoolgirl.

"Thank goodness I found you, they want you and Ed in Marketing."

Machine gun fire crackles out in No Man's Land. Whistles blow, far
off. Not our division.

"Yell-o." Willie says the word repeatedly, like trying a combination
lock. "Yeah-low." "Yell-o-wah!"

Willie hits me with a barrage of yellow, so I take off—I am on a mission. I'm supposed to find Ed and Willie and tell them something. Or
was it bring them somewhere? I forget.

I find Ed in a forward gun position. He's slumped in the mud like
only a dead guy would slump. I turn him over. He's riddled with Sharpies, a whole multi-color pack. "Bastards!" They even removed the safety
caps.

All I can think of is that Ed will never straighten that slice out now.
Ed died a slicer.

Bruce, Accounting too, comes up behind me, "Ed?" I nod. "Shit.
Well, it could've been worse."

"How could it possibly have been worse?" I ask him.

"It could've been me."

In the trenches, we take everything we can get our hands on. Like
water, the best place to carry drugs is in the body. No one has heard
from HQ lately. There is a lot of talk. Who ordered this birthday cake?
Where do all these drugs come from? The drugs are a godsend though;
they make worries like these just float away.

At night during the commercials, I think about my kids. I sing to
myself, a song I used to sing them about a man who sees his lover's
face in the reflection on a snow-covered mountain. I sang this to them,
selfishly, so that when they see a mountain they'll think of me. And so,
when they have a really tough problem, they can just look at a hill or
snow or a thing that reflects other things and it'll remind them they're
not alone. Sometimes at night I see their faces on the white mountains

that lie beyond the enemy pillboxes.

Deeper in the trenches, I find Jimbo, on loan from the International Division. He's brandishing a label gun indiscriminately. The safety is definitely off, because red labels are spitting all around.

Whump!!

An HP Laser Jet II slams into the ground in front of our foxhole, showering us with dirt and plastic paper tray shards. Jimbo jumps up, screaming, "Die, cocksuckers, die!" and sprays labels into No Man's Land.

The wind flutters them back at us, and I read them as they snowflake down. "Pow-Wow." "Mangle the Guru poodle cup." "Finalize the win-win situation." "The marketing secretary has huge tubes and a tight package." "Strategize the follow-up meeting." "Pow-Wow" (again).

Here, I sort of lose my shit and laugh uncontrollably as I slip into a daydream I keep having. I am on KP and we're serving a choice of either langoustines or rat. I am cleaning the langoustines, breaking them in the middle and tossing the shrimpheads in a garbage bin and then the tails in after them. There's nothing in the langoustines pot, so everyone orders rat. Martha Stewart is there too, dressed as Annie Oakley with six-shooters and fringe, the whole nine yards, shelling the langoustines alongside me and giving pointers on how to grill them.

When I get hold of myself, I set out again. I have to tell Joe Haskell about Ed and Willie. This will not be good. I head back through the trench system. It is a hub-and-spoke design, with Marketing as the hub. At the hub, I find Joe Haskell in the Situation Room pouring over battle plans. He slides red and blue pieces on a boardmap with a long stick and punches formulas into his HP-12C calculator. Joe is an inspiring sight, slicked black hair, expensive retro spectacles, red power tie in a crisp Windsor—you can tell he's never felt more alive than in this very moment.

At first Marketing used a Risk board for our planning sessions. And we marveled at the marshalling of forces and the plans with arrows and pincer movements sweeping across the Eurasian theatre. We used Irkutz as our base of operations for a hub-and-spoke system on a grand scale. There was buy in from all departments. Then, after the first operations failed to achieve their objectives, we right-sized and switched to a roadmap and those little green army men. But it was too confusing with our guys and their guys both being green and all. Now, we just use a regular Stratego board.

Joe Haskell takes the news of Ed and Willie very hard. He flings the Stratego board against the side of the bunker. Blue and red pieces fly about dangerously, with all those sharp corners.

"Well, you're senior accountant now," he tells me. "You fucking deal with the paperwork."

Joe never used to swear. According to the manual, it is strictly forbidden in the workplace.

Joe grabs his rifle and helmet and jumps on the Situation Room table. He peers down at all of us, support staff, tired guys lying against the wall, marketing analysts, guys with earphones receiving and relaying critical information.

"All right everyone, listen up," he shouts. "Rustle up a gun. Ammunition. We are taking that hill!"

He has a gleam in his eye. Joe sees himself as a man who takes hills. He has an MBA from a top school, he is a wiz with PowerPoint, he makes appropriate hand gestures when he speaks. And he runs out of the bunker. We look at each other with flittery rabbit eyes. We follow Joe Haskell. I run with them, yelling "Yeah!" and "Kill!" like they do. You just have to get psyched up for climbing out into No Man's Land.

Joe Haskell stops at Little Willie's sandbag. Words are exchanged. He's trying to get Willie to buy into his impromptu take-the-hill plan. I'm too far back to hear, but I see Joe's face redden and spittle fly. Then Joe runs on. I guess spitting on Willie was draining the momentum of our attack. As we run by, Little Willie shoots us in the back. "Grrrreen." "Ba-loo!"

I trudge along behind the pack, then duck into a corner. I take out a company logo pen and pad. I have to write Ed's performance review; I feel the weight of the responsibility. But sitting here now, I can't think. What can you say? What did my last review say? Shit! I've never written one of these. I am not qualified for this. *Ed worked well with others.* Yeah, that's good. *Ed took on responsibilities beyond the roles and responsibilities of his job.* No, not good, can't use responsibilities twice like that. What's another word for responsibilities? Roles? Fuck! *Ed always came to meet-*

ings with an extra pen. Excellent! *He was a good soldier, even though he wasn't supposed to smoke in the forward gun position, which was probably why the sniper hit him with the Sharpies. Worked well with others.* Rolling now. *Soft and filled with squishy red tubes and sacs dying to get out. A wellspring of ideas for improvements and efficiencies we'll never know.*

Overhead, the hideous screech of faxes.

"Incoming!!!"

I smush further into the corner of sandbags. I look off and try not to think about the shelling. The mountains in the distance are tall and abrupt. They rise up confidently, miles past the battle, like they're reaching up to pull down the sun. I don't recognize them. I have never seen these mountains, even in pictures or movies or books. They are foreign, alien, they cannot possibly be ours. Whose are they? Where the *fuck* are we?

I drop the pad. I throw the company pen into No Man's Land and slide down in the mud. My boss, Joe Haskell, used to come into my cubicle, back when I had one, and ask me to do things, and he'd promise if I did them everything would be great. "That would be great," he'd say, like a mantra or a magical incantation. Well, I did them. I always did those things for Joe. But you know, that's just it, nothing ever did turn out great.

Land of Dead Babies

by Rebecca Cook

This poem is about dead babies. There are dead babies everywhere.

Dead babies can be very ugly. They do not look good in pictures or wastebaskets.
They make terrible billboards and posters. But made into shoes they become beautiful,
into sweaters and purses and jackets and jeans. Dead babies make the best jeans.

Dead babies can be very useful. They're pretty good missile weapons and
if you can find enough of them, they make excellent ground cover.

I know a man who crushes dead babies into mirrors and calls them art.
I know a woman who sews dead babies into lampshades for history lessons.

Do you know that the president always wears ties made of dead babies?
They whisper to him while he speechifies, he fumbles and they laugh.

Dead baby laughter is not funny.

No one likes to hear their goo-goo-gaaing and gurgling.
Nobody wants to hear a dead baby whisper.
At important functions, wise hostesses distribute ear plugs.
During sermons, fierce praying drowns them out.

Some dead babies have been genetically modified to resemble your sisters and brothers.
Some dead babies have been pulled from black hats and resemble doves.

Me, I hate all these dead babies stuck to my clothes. I've tried everything to wash them away but they leave terrible stains. Usually I just chuck them out, but even under plastic dead babies cause a terrible ruckus.

But some dead babies are great for snacking, the calories have been calculated and are low. And that dead baby taste, can't beat it. Whenever I need to, I pull a dead baby out and smoke it and I feel so much better.

Aubade with a Quincy Jones Biography on PBS

by Barbara Duffey

In response to Pound's "The Garret"

Dawn came in like Philip Marlowe
drunk on rye and gray with stubble.
You called in sick and I took you
to the pharmacy. Michael asked,
"How's your wife?" ringing up your drugs.
You've never told him that I'm not
your wife. The Texas Family Code,
line 2.401, declares
we're married if we represent
to others that we're married (check),
we live together (check), and we
agree to be married.
Between aneurisms, Quincy
and his girlfriend from the *Mod Squad*
married so she'd gain legal rights
to his remains, her grip of him
wouldn't cremate in the L.A.
County Morgue. Come, let us pity
the married and the unmarried.

He didn't die either time, but
I turn from the TV to look
at dear you, not my husband nor
my unhusband, eyes glazed over
like cakes. Cohabitation
and public display of marriage
should not be seen to constitute
an agreement to be married.
I dole your dose and brew your tea.
What life has better than this hour
of waking together: this power
To guarantee your body lies
With me till I say otherwise.

The Greatest Minds of Our Generation Are Designing PlayStations

Barrelhousing with Malcolm Gladwell

art by Cecelia Ferriera

Admit it: over the past couple of years, you've used the phrase "the tipping point" in a conversation. Maybe it's only been once or twice, but you know you've done it. Moreover, you probably thought you were making some extremely salient comment at the time, like "I heard my garbage men raving about *Heroes* the other day, so I think it's finally gone past the tipping point." It's probably safe to say that the phrase "the tipping point" went past its own tipping point some time in late 2000, not long after the publication of—you guessed it, Sparky—*The Tipping Point*. Malcolm Gladwell's book was an instant phenomenon, entering the minds of millions like a highly contagious disease—which (considering the fact that the book is *about* how ideas spread like viruses) is sort of like sharks appearing magically all up and down both coasts a few months after the publication of *Jaws*.

By the time his second book, *Blink*, appeared on bookstore shelves, Gladwell had become a kind of pop-literati icon, a man "in the know," an insider whose job seems to be to help us understand the bizarre human mind and its many manifestations in sports, entertainment, science, business, and everyday life. His articles in the *New Yorker* are practically required reading—the absolute bare minimum for cultural literacy—and his readings and speaking engagements are sold out, standing room only affairs. To paraphrase Christopher Walken on *Saturday Night Live*, America has a fever, and the only prescription is more Gladwell. With that in mind, *Barrelhouse* poetry editor Gwydion Suilebhan was thrilled to play pharmacist.

Gwydion Suilebhan: It used to be that if you were a writer who wrote about science, you were almost automatically branded a big old nerd. Think of Johnny Carson mocking Carl Sagan's somewhat nasal voice. ("Billions and billions...") Now, however, science writers seem super-hip all of a sudden: we halfway expect to see you and, say, Steven Levitt laughing in your seats together at the next Oscar awards ceremony, or to read a gossip item about Richard Preston and Jared Diamond canoodling in some nightclub with Paris and Nicole. What do you think has brought about this change?

Malcolm Gladwell: Well, Sagan wrote about astronomy and physics—which are the nerdy sciences—and the big topics these days for science writers are economics, anthropology, and psychology, which all have humans in them. I think what's changed as well is that writers have found ways to tell compelling stories about science. Remember *Hot Zone*, from ten years or so ago? I think of that as a real breakthrough book, along with some of Michael Crichton's science-y thrillers, all of which introduce scientific topics into the popular narrative arsenal.

GS: During the last couple of decades or so, science books have perennially topped the nonfiction bestseller lists: everything from *Blink* and *The Tipping Point* (of course) to *Guns, Germs, and Steel* and *Freakonomics*. Even, if you want to go far back enough, *The Hot Zone* and *Awakenings*. On the fiction bestseller lists, however, science doesn't seem to be of interest whatsoever. We seem to care a lot more about magicians and illusionists, for example, than we do about scientists. We have Harry Potter, *Jonathan Strange & Mr. Norrell*, and *The Amazing Adventures of Kavalier and Clay*, but few (if any) heroic biologists, tragic sociologists, or sexy physicists. What is it about science, do you think, that makes novelists—or, even poets, for that matter—find it difficult or impossible with which to engage?

MG: I feel like certain kinds of science topics were very much in vogue thirty or forty years ago. Between the A-bomb, Sputnik, and the Apollo program, there was a scientific mythology that could be exploited by fiction. But now the central science figure is doing something a good deal less glamorous: he or she is writing computer code. And what do you do with that if you're a novelist? It's not like trying to walk on the moon, or blow up the world. Fifty years ago, the greatest minds of our generation went to Los Alamos. Today they design PlayStations.

GS: Have either *Blink* or *The Tipping Point* been optioned for the big screen? We find ourselves wondering what Charlie Kaufman might do with either book, given his success with Susan Orleans' *The Orchid Thief* in his film *Adaptation*.

MG: *Blink* has been sold to Stephen Gaghan, who won an Oscar for *Traffic* and wrote and directed *Syriana*. He and I dreamt up a storyline taken from the book that, if the truth be told, has almost nothing to do with the book in the end. It's all in Stephen's very capable hands at the moment. My view is that it would be foolish to try and tell an Oscar winner what to do.

GS: Our world is increasingly scientific—and it all seems to be moving too quickly for lots of people. The development of new medical treatments, new insights about the structure of the universe, new energy sources, new data about the environment—they all seem to outpace the public's ability to understand them. The cutting edge of science has never been farther away from the top of the bell curve of general scientific literacy—let alone from the buckle in the middle of the Bible belt. How does this affect your job as a science writer? Do you have to work harder to translate what you've learned from the experts into a language accessible by the masses?

MG: Not really. Because, remember, the floor has risen as well. Anyone who has been to college has at least a rudimentary understanding of the outlines of most scientific arguments. I mean, I can talk about a virus or artificial intelligence or relatively complex psychological experiments and presume a fairly sophisticated knowledge of the principles of those topics. I'm not sure that was true forty or fifty years ago. I think we forget sometimes just how well-educated the general population is these days.

GS: Okay, we agree that the general population is probably better educated than we generally assume. (The Intelligent Design movement, however, does make us wonder; though perhaps it's really best seen as a kind of collective, willfully ignorant creativity that allows a logically flawed worldview to be constructed out of vapor—an intelligent bit of artifice that should be treated like a piece of fiction, rather than a sign of stupidity.) Still, how do you explain, say, the increasing gaps between the math test scores of children in the United States and those of children in other countries? Are other countries getting smarter faster than we are?

MG: They are certainly taking more math than we are, which is slightly different from saying that they are getting smarter. There is also a very complicated technical debate over how to interpret cross-national test score comparisons, since in the U.S. everyone takes standardized tests and in other countries only those students streamed into college-entry courses tend to take standardized tests—so it's not apples and apples. But the math problem is real. In fact, I've spent the last couple of weeks reading extensively about math, believe it or not. The question of how to teach it, and what it means not to take advanced math, turns out to be surprisingly interesting.

GS: Intellectual throwdown: you vs. James Gleick, author of *Chaos, Faster,* and *Genius,* among other major works of popular science. Who wins?

MG: Oh, Gleick. I met him once at a dinner party. By the time the appetizers were finished I was hiding under the table. The dude ran circles around me. I actually think his masterwork is his Richard Feynman biography.

GS: How about you vs. Dava Sobel, who wrote *Longitude* and *The Planets* and *Galileo's Daughter*? Come on, you know you want to answer.

MG: I would have to go with Sobel. The secret truth is that I'm a bit of a lightweight. I feel like people like Sobel and Gleick spend their free time in the archives somewhere, poring over nineteenth-century texts on the microfiche reader, whereas I spend my free time watching college football.

GS: What did you think when The Roots named their sixth album *The Tipping Point*? Did that moment in cultural history represent the tipping point of *The Tipping Point*? (We are sorry, for what it's worth, that they decided to go with *Game Theory* for their next release. We were rooting, pun intended, for *Blink*.)

MG: It's safe to say that was the high point of my life. You know, I interviewed The Roots on stage, at the New Yorker Festival last year. Questlove was sitting next to me. And he took one look at me and my hair, reached into his own (even bigger) afro, pulled out a pick, and wordlessly handed it to me. That, I believe, is what is called being "schooled." He owned the crowd from that point on.

GS: The ideas you describe in both *Blink* and *The Tipping Point* have succeeded in entering popular discourse rapidly and easily. Unlike other recent science books—Jared Diamond's *Collapse* comes to mind, or anything by Laurie Garrett—they seem not only to capture the zeitgeist and to be broadly accessible, but also to echo in our minds while we live our daily lives. (Having just read *Blink*, for example, you might get a stack of resumes on your desk and wonder whether you should have your secretary black out each applicant's name so as not to be prejudiced by gender or racial assumptions.) Is this a quality you strive to achieve in your work? Does it come naturally to you? Does it depend, at least in part, on the subjects you choose to write about? And how do you choose those subjects?

MG: All good questions, and all questions that I can't really answer. I simply write about things that interest me, and hope and pray that others will be equally interested. There's no system other than that. And no one is as baffled by the success of those books as I am. How do I choose my subjects? Usually desperation. Someone tells me something. I make a zillion phone calls and ransack the library and try and flesh it out.

GS: You say desperation makes you choose your subjects, and we suddenly have this image of you as a high school student (on a program like, say, *Saved by the Bell* or *That 70s Show*), scrambling madly to get a term paper in on time. Or maybe like MacGyver or Hannibal Smith (of the *A-Team*, a Barrelhouse favorite), improvising madly to concoct a solution to a pesky deadline problem. Which of course makes us wonder: where is your desperation taking you next? What's the next Gladwell book we'll be wishing we'd written ourselves?

MG: I wish I knew! I know I have to start by January, and I have some vague ideas. But nothing that has coalesced into a book yet. Funny you should mention *MacGyver*: I once knew a guy who had broken down all the different *MacGyver* archetypes. (I think there were five.) It was quite brilliant. It had to be the oddest television show of its era.

GS: You've read and reviewed Steven Johnson's *Everything Bad Is Good for You*, a book which argues that pop culture might actually be making people smarter. At Barrelhouse, we're kind of in love with popular culture. We've made it our mission to find high-quality writing—fiction, poetry, and nonfiction—that engages with pop culture in a thoughtful, inspiring way. Man, though, that is one *hard* mission. Most writers seem to think of pop culture as a sort of shameful indulgence—we're only allowed to watch *Lost*, and only if we deconstruct the show's symbolism during commercial breaks. God forbid we should tune into—let alone enjoy—*Project Runway*. So what do you think? Are we nuts, or are we onto something?

MG: No. You're right. This actually touches on a big theme of mine. I think that a lot of criticism or commentary these days has lost the ability to simply enjoy art for what it is. I just read Michael Lewis's new book, *The Blind Side*, which made me cry and brought me an incalculable amount of joy. And then I read the review in *The New York Times*, which conceded that he is a great storyteller and then proceeded to nitpick about reconstructed conversations and technical issues. It made me want to scream. Whatever happened to just sitting down with a book or TV show and letting yourself get swept away? I have, for example, read every Jack Reacher thriller by Lee Child, in galleys, and if any pointy head tells me that he's a derivative pulp writer who endlessly reworks the same tired themes or some such, I think I'll jump off a cliff.

GS: Who's a better hero for our age: Superman, an immigrant who has thoroughly assimilated and adopted American values; Batman, a self-made man who relies on cutting-edge technology to supplement his humanity; Wolverine, a genetic mutant who embodies the spirit of the conservative angry white male; or Spider-Man, a teenage kid overwhelmed by the changes he's going through and the twisted adults out to get him at every turn?

MG: Very, very interesting question. As a kid I would have said Spidey for certain. Or maybe Iron Man, although in retrospect all the problems he had with his heart make him seem a bit Dick Cheney-like. But it's really Superman who I think we long for the most. In the midst of all this crazy anti-immigrant talk, it would be useful to remind everyone that it's the newcomers from distant lands who have superpowers and who save us from evil. Where would an America-first movement have gotten Gotham? The answer is "in trouble."

GS: Were you paying attention to what happened with the recent movie *Snakes on a Plane*? Seemed like it tipped so hard that the movie itself became of secondhand importance: the buzz about the movie was the real story. Have we so completely detached from art that we don't actually need to experience it to experience it?

MG: I think the short answer is that we don't need to experience art if the art in question is *Snakes on a Plane*. I remember something an art executive once told me: nothing is so dangerous as a great campaign for a bad product.

GS: Back in the good old days, people who liked football were usually interested in the simple values one associates (probably inaccurately) with the good people of the conservative American Midwest: loyalty, teamwork, faith, obedience, and a bit of casual violence thrown into the mix. Baseball, on the other hand, attracted liberal eggheads who were more interested in statistics than in excitement and action. (Not to mention a few poets who waxed rhapsodic about, say, fields of dreams.) With the advent of fantasy football, however, pigskins and number crunching have made an odd marriage of sorts. People who wouldn't have admitted to spending Sundays on the couch eating Doritos are now debating whether to start Tom Brady against the Bears defense—with their mothers. Which leaves us wondering: can you help us figure out what the heck's behind this magical transformation? Does it have any significance at all? Does it help us understand the fictitious nature of the red state/blue state split? Does it serve as a cautionary tale for the ability of technology to soften violence? Help us figure this one out.

MG: I may be too deeply inside this particular phenomenon to have any great insight into it. The fact is that football got "gourmetified," the way olive oil and salt and spaghetti sauce did. It went upscale, because all of a sudden there was a group of highly educated, middle class and upper middle class people who wanted *more* from it. And the great thing about football is that it could give you more. I say this, by the way, as someone who got irritated recently because ESPN.com took until Wednesday to post their NFL Power Rankings. What's up with that? Do they know how many hours I killed waiting to find out whether the Patriots' victory over the Bengals would make them the number one team in the league? (It should have, by the way.)

GS: And finally, to end where all Barrelhouse interviews must end: what's your favorite Patrick Swayze movie?

MG: Really, really tough question. Some part of me wants to say *Road House*. But not *Dirty Dancing*, if only because that movie is all about Jennifer Grey, who was an absolute goddess until she had a nose job. Why did she have a nose job? Does that make any sense at all?

GS: No, Jennifer Grey's nose job doesn't make any sense—none at all. Then again, does any purely cosmetic plastic surgery every really work much? The results only look good on television with the right lighting and excellent makeup. Perhaps it explains why celebrities are typically so reclusive. How in the heck do these people not scare children away in public? How do they ever get any dates?

MG: I've wondered about this too. Is it maybe that we only notice bad plastic surgery? Someone once told me that if you start really, really young and get a steady diet of very subtle alterations done over time, no one will notice. But that's depressing, right? Because it's clearly already too late for me.

pop flotsam. cultural jetsam.
ROCK POSTER SKETCHES

by Jay Ryan of the Bird Machine
www.thebirdmachine.com

42   Barrelhouse

Sometimes Women Have Greater Portions of Learning Than Wisdom Which Is No Better Use to Them Than a Maynsale to a Fly Boat

by Eva Hooker

Which is like the woman who bundles her flaming
hair in woven gray silk then fears to let it slip its interval
and care lest it spill
and cast upon her
cradled book a shadow and draw
out the conjunctions of herself
Which is like the young girl who recites all from memory
the entry on crocodile tears she found in the long hall: they who eat their prey
weep after
Which is like the she-bear who in the safe winter of her secrecy
frames with her tongue, licks out of her own substance a likeness
a leggy flowering
(littered blind in the third month
fore-feet folded up like a fist);
Which is why, she, being almost dazzled by alembic
dark coming again into light, seems to stagger
like the newly widowed—
And then, by reason of long fasting, reels for straightness and mercy

When I Ask My Friend Susan Why She Doesn't Like Oatmeal, She Tells Me This Story

by Amorak Huey

I don't remember much about the church,
but the sky over Notre Dame was the color of lead
the day I learned oil and water don't mix. Rainbows
slid across puddles in the parking lot,
uncertain reflections, shimmering amoeba shapes
holier to me than any building. My own face stared
out at me like a stranger, some other child trapped
in shallow water. I didn't want to believe
my mother's explanation, although I never forgot
and it is pleasing to know miracles
are born even in the sludge that drips from tailpipes.
I skinned my knee somewhere near Canterbury,
lost a baby tooth in a tent outside the walls of Rabat,
finally learned to pop my gum
in the chill halls of the Louvre. This did not please my mother,
who spun and hissed she'd send me home.
I dared her to, changing forever
who I am to her, and she to me,
though she claims no memory of such a moment.
It was their honeymoon, but we missed
our cruise ship over, settling
instead for cramped passage on a foreign freighter.

Ordered to get to know each other,
we kids spent days banished to the deck
where we learned to spit, and swear in Slavic. I was seven,
lost somewhere in the middle.
England, France, Morocco, Spain —
we were abroad nine months in all
and ate the same overdone oatmeal at every breakfast,
the same zucchini-tomato-mush for supper.
My mother didn't trust the local food.
Even today when she comes to see her grandkids,
she brings along a jar of peanut butter,
a brand I won't buy because of too much sugar.
My stepfather had sawed apart one of his pianos
so he could practice each morning,
the severed keyboard balanced
on the back bumper of our VW camper,
his fingers charging through a silent symphony,
a dark flash in his eye, a violent lifting of his head.
Still, I always knew when he missed a note.

art by Mike Fitts

THE GREAT ESCAPE

BY PETE MACDONALD

*If I want to be completely honest, art (not just the art of the cinema)
is for me unimportant.*
   —Ingmar Bergman

*Wrong entertainment lowers the whole living condition and moral
ideals of a race.*
   —The Motion Picture Production Code of 1930

American movie audiences love spectacle,
excitement, adventure. Larger-than-life superheroes like
Spider-Man, Batman, and Christ work their improbable magic year after year on multiplex screens throughout the country, dazzling us with
their web-slinging, their outrageously cool cars and amazing gadgets,
their almighty bravado. Blockbuster Hollywood movies are written,
produced, and directed to satisfy our craving for astonishment, for stu-
pefaction, for *miracles*, to allow us to escape—if just for a couple of
hours—the reality of our day-to-day lives. And what's so wrong with
that? These movies are intended to be more like amusement park rides
than ponderous strolls through art galleries, and just as one shouldn't
fault a carnival operator for providing mindless diversion, anyone who
criticizes Hollywood for doing the same thing is completely missing the
point: *it's all about the money—always was and always will be.* One glance

at a list of the top fifty highest grossing movies of all time proves beyond a doubt that successful blockbusters pay the bills in Hollywood. Moreover, huge box office successes not only compensate for the flops, they provide studios capital to invest in the occasional production intended for the more serious-minded, or "art-house," audience. But Steve Almond, in a vituperative essay called "Burn Hollywood" published in the premiere issue of *Barrelhouse*, claims that the act of watching an escapist movie is "a waste of consciousness." We must suppose this is time better spent at the library, or listening to NPR, or going to yoga class—all admirable pursuits. But is watching *Lara Croft: Tomb Raider* really the same, metaphysically, as tweaking out on methamphetamine?

While it is wonderful when a movie can provide us with deeper insight into the sad reality of our day-to-day plight, it is also a gift when we can go into a dark theater and, for two hours or so, be entertained in ways that take us *away* from that struggle, transport us into Oz, as it were, and help us forget for a while our impending divorces, or the credit card bills we can't pay, or the jobs we hate. Escapist movies provide a respite in which we experience vicarious thrills impossible to enjoy any other way. The value of movies like these is wholly subjective, proportional to the amount of enjoyment provided the individual viewer. It is also aesthetically subjective, and critics can argue about the failings of mindless movies all they want, but box office records reveal that the audiences for these films don't give a damn what critics think.

With that in mind, I'll recount the following "waste of consciousness" anecdote: my brain sizzled like those fried eggs you used to see on the old *Just Say No!* drug posters; I had been working at the furthest edges of my consciousness nonstop for two weeks, writing a paper for the most difficult graduate seminar in philosophy I'd ever taken, and I'd just completed the final draft. The last thing in the world I wanted to do was *think*. My roommate happened to come home a few minutes later, saw me sitting at the computer in a persistent vegetative state, and said, "Hey, you wanna go see *Romy and Michelle's High School Reunion*? Mira Sorvino and Lisa Kudrow play these ditzy L.A. chicks who go to their ten-year high school reunion."

"That sounds *perfect*," I said.

And it was. A delightfully loopy movie that required nothing of its viewers but to sit back and enjoy the silliness. Was it "art"? Not if your definition requires, as a necessary (but not necessarily sufficient) condition, that it provide important insight into the "human condition," or that it lead to prolonged discussion about normative ethical theory, or that it make you cry. Did I care whether it was "art?" Not for a minute. All I wanted was to have some fun.

Here's a short list of a few more superbly meaningless films that come to mind—in no particular order—if you have some consciousness to spare: *There's Something About Mary, Dirty Dancing, Swingers, Basic Instinct, Titanic* (requires extra spare consciousness due to length and cheesiness), *Caddyshack, Zoolander, Pirates of the Caribbean: The Curse of the Black Pearl, Pirates of the Caribbean: Dead Man's Chest* (and I'll go out on a limb and recommend Part III of this endearing triumvirate of falderal one year before its release: who can resist seeing Keith Richards play Johnny Depp's *dad?*), *Wayne's World, Bill and Ted's Excellent Adventure, Charlie's Angels.*

Almond's essay is, for the most part, a whiney, *ad hominum* diatribe against Hollywood; it comes across as deeply personal and embittered, apparently stemming from his disappointment with the "sad and lost" Hollywood business folk with whom he, for a time, discussed the possibility of turning his book of stories, *My Life in Heavy Metal,* into a movie. In the midst of the histrionics, he succeeds in making a valid, if obvious point: Hollywood produces a lot of lousy, soulless movies, and those involved in the individual productions speak of them as if they were high art. While this is certainly true (and is almost always a contractual obligation agreed to long before the movie is made), in Almond's world this practice is not just *bad,* it is morally, ethically, and aesthetically unforgivable. After all, Hollywood's mission—the "mission of art"—is "to keep the pathways of the heart open, to reveal the painful and absurd truth of our lives…" (*Romy and Michelle* made me laugh out loud, but it certainly didn't do *that!*). Almond spreads the blame around, but emphasizes various actors' complicity in the industry's alleged turn away from "art" and toward big profits.

He calls Robert DeNiro a "punk" and Russell Crowe and Jim Carey "whores."

In one passage, Almond argues that escapist movies allow moviegoers "to retreat from the emotional duties of real life." What, in the name of Cecil B. DeMille, are life's "emotional duties?" Are they the same as ethical duties? Moral duties? If not, how are they different? Do I actually have a *duty* to feel a given emotion in a given situation? Who gets to decide what *that* is? And what—if any such thing as an "emotional duty" actually exists and can be said to have relevance to one's *entertainment* dollar—is so terribly wrong with occasionally *shirking* that duty and having a good time at the movies? Would that be as subversive as, say, cutting class?

The Art v. Commerce debate has been raging about Hollywood at varying degrees of intensity since the 1910s, when intellectuals such as Randolph Bourne began writing about their initial experiences at the movies. Bourne wrote that he felt a "certain unholy glee at [the] wholesale rejection" of the hoity-toity culture of the times, but he also stated that moviegoers "seem to be witnessing a lowbrow snobbery…as tyrannical and arrogant as the other culture of universities and millionaires and museums." His solution—echoed by many respected thinkers over the last ninety-odd years—was a kind of middle road, in which movies would uplift people while simultaneously entertaining them.

Easier said than done.

There are great eras in music, literature, the fine arts. And there are great eras in movies. This is not a great movie era by any stretch of the imagination, and any intelligent discussion about the current "state of the cinema" in Hollywood has to take this into account. The movie gods are not smiling on us the way they were in, say, the 1950s or 1970s. This is not to say there haven't been glimpses of excellence that will likely survive the decade. *Lost in Translation* and *Eternal Sunshine of the Spotless Mind* come immediately to mind.

But compare: here is a list of some of the movies Hollywood produced between 1950 and 1955: *The Asphalt Jungle, Sunset Boulevard, All About Eve, A Streetcar Named Desire, The African Queen, Singin' in the Rain, High Noon, Shane, Rear Window, A Place in the Sun, From Here to Eternity, On the Waterfront, East of Eden, Rebel Without a Cause.* Here are a few movies released between 1970 and 1975: *The Godfather, and The Godfather: Part II, Chinatown, Dog Day Afternoon, Cabaret, De-*

liverance, American Graffiti, Mean Streets, Five Easy Pieces, Taxi Driver, The Conversation, The French Connection, Serpico, One Flew Over the Cuckoo's Nest. Almost anyone would agree that these are excellent films; at least a few of them are timeless classics. If you disagree with this statement, wait a few years, then see them again.

Now make your own list of great movies released between 2000 and 2005. Pretty depressing. There are at least two possible reasons for this. There either isn't the talent out there to dazzle us—Scorcese, Coppola, et. al. have "dried up," a la Paul McCartney—or the talent is there but the *audience* is not, leading to the sad conclusion that great filmmakers are unable to get the green light for their "art" films, and instead are forced to make, for example, *The Aviator*. (And all the new geniuses are driving cabs, or worse, directing sitcoms.)

No matter which theory you choose, one thing is as clear today as it has been since people began flocking to the ubiquitous Nickleodeons: Hollywood will make, or try to make, what the public wants, or at least what it *thinks* the public wants. And while the audience for thoughtful drama (or thoughtful comedy for that matter) has almost always been small compared to the audience for spectacle, what distinguishes the "great" movie eras from the mediocre ones isn't that *fewer bad* movies are made, but that *more great* ones are. (For example, in the 1990s—an uninspired decade for movies if ever there was one—Hollywood released, on average, at least one movie every day, or approximately 3,850 films. Were there more than ten or twenty good ones? How many great ones? *Dead Man Walking* and what else? *Schindler's List;* maybe *Short Cuts;* probably two or three others.)

The majority of movies in any given year are pretty terrible. Why is that? First, it's damned hard to make a good movie, let alone a great one. As screenwriter William Goldman points out in *Which Lie Did I Tell?*, his highly entertaining and informative sequel to *Adventures in the Screen Trade*, the most important work on a movie happens before shooting starts—preparing the screenplay and completing the casting. If you've done those things right, you have a shot at a successful movie. But, Goldman writes, "If you have made a grievous error in either script or casting, you are dead in the water."

When millions of shareholders' dollars are at stake, as well as various egomaniacs' reputations, mistakes are easy to make. Consider that the part of Rick in *Casablanca* was once slated to be played by Ronald Reagan; that Jon Voight almost didn't get the part of Joe Buck in *Midnight Cowboy*; that Paramount executives made Marlon Brando *audition* for the part of Vito Corleone; that *Chinatown* was a near disaster until the original score was replaced by Jerry Goldsmith's magnificent, soulful, trumpet-based jazz. Upon seeing a sneak preview of *The Wizard of Oz*, a group of high-level Metro-Goldwyn-Mayer executives wanted to *cut* "Somewhere Over the Rainbow," thinking it was a lousy song that would bore the audience. And look at *Ishtar, Waterworld, Heaven's Gate, The Postman*, each one an embarrassing disaster. A lot of experienced, talented people thought those movies would not only be good, but were convinced they'd show a substantial profit.

In an early scene in *Sunset Boulevard*—one of Hollywood's best efforts at self-deprecation—former silent-movie queen Norma Desmond asks failed screenwriter Joe Gillis about his screenplays. He replies, "The last one I wrote was about Oakies in the dust bowl. You'd never know it because when it reached the screen the whole thing played on a torpedo boat." It is a funny, revealing comment on the surreal aspects of the collaborative nature of filmmaking. A lot of input from a lot of people goes into decision-making in Hollywood; sometimes it ends in catastrophe, and other times, well, you end up with *Sunset Boulevard*.

Another reason movies are generally lousy, and I would argue the most important reason, is that Hollywood is not now, and never has been, in the business of making "art." It is in the business of trying to put people in theater seats by nearly any means possible. (We've all seen pictures of 1950s audiences wearing 3D glasses—technology designed to out-tech television, which was perceived by the movie industry as a grave threat.) If a little "art" happens along the way, so much the better, but, to the detriment of humankind or not, art is beside the point.

In "Burn Hollywood," Almond sounds a lot like the fictitious film director John L. Sullivan in Preston Sturges' 1941 comedy *Sullivan's Travels*. Sullivan directs light-hearted comedies and is plagued with a desire to make "meaningful" films, films that would accurately depict the ruin of American lives in the midst of the depression. Sullivan is a highly successful director, living in a mansion, breathing the thin air of those who live life in the stratosphere—the wealthiest Hollywood elite. He decides to research the life of the poor by becoming a hobo for a couple of weeks. He meets the beautiful Veronica Lake along the way, who plays a failed actress generous enough to buy the "hobo" breakfast, and together they experience the sad existence of America's transients.

The last third of the movie is a bit darker than what you'd expect from a forties comedy. Through a series of mishaps Sullivan suffers a bout of amnesia and is sentenced to six years of hard labor for assaulting a railroad employee. One night the prisoners are allowed to see a movie in a nearby local church. In a moving sequence that is arguably more powerful today due to sixty years of historical perspective on racial oppression, a black preacher leads his poor Southern congregation through a Robesonesque version of "Let My People Go" while the prisoners are led into the church in chains. They watch a Mickey Mouse cartoon and the men and the churchgoers all break out into rousing, infectious laughter. For everyone in the church, it is as if a great weight has been lifted from their shoulders, albeit temporarily. In spite of himself, Sullivan laughs along with all the others at Pluto's problems with flypaper, and in the process realizes the value of simple entertainment. Soon thereafter he is released from prison and he returns to making comedies, turning down an opportunity to direct a more "serious" film called *O Brother Where Art Thou?* (The Coen brothers' movie of the same name is taken from this scene.)

Sullivan's Travels is Sturges's message to the missionaries: lighten up and realize that entertainment can be just as important as "art."

Almond claims that the real problem with the awful state of American movies "resides with us, the viewing public." In other words, if we'd just stop patronizing the fun, mindless stuff, and save our movie money for films that "leave aside all that is false and inessential" (you may ask: *according to whom?*) Hollywood would make only films that are meant to help, not hinder our collective and individual efforts to *evolve*, to not be so "frightened by the shadow of our own souls." More importantly, we, as a people, would presumably begin to engage in meaningful moral discourse; our world would become less violent, less contrived, and more emotionally robust.

Wouldn't it be great if things were that simple?

I imagine that *Crash*, winner of the 2006 Academy Award for Best Picture, is exactly the kind of film Almond is talking about. It makes a valiant attempt to teach us all about racism; in fact, it should have been called *Racism Is Bad*. It appears to have been designed to "awaken our capacities for mercy" (to plagiarize another Almond phrase). Instead, it awakened my gag reflex: the movie's didacticism is relentless, insufferable. For the entire ninety-odd minutes of the film, I felt as though I were being beaten over the head with rolled up copies of "We Shall Overcome." Almost any two-minute sketch on *Chappelle's Show* contains more profound insights into the continuing problem of racism in this country.

Here's another anecdote, this one as mystifying to me as *Crash* beating *Brokeback Mountain* or *Capote:* my two friends and I—he was from a small town in Illinois and she was his girlfriend from Yorkshire, England—wanted to go to a movie. We checked the *Village Voice* and saw that *The Bicycle Thief* was playing at Theater 80 St. Marks. They'd never heard of the film; I convinced them to go. It was a rainy night and we took a cab over to the theater. On the way, Ms. Yorkshire expressed grave doubt about the decision to see this prosaically titled movie. "But this is one of the greatest movies ever made," I said. "Trust me." My Illinois friend said, "You'd better be right," as if something important depended on it. Two hours later we left the theater, profoundly affected. Once again, I was moved, shaken, had to wipe the tears away. But they'd *hated* it, viciously berating me for dragging them out in the rain "to see that piece of shit." We never went to a movie together again.

There's no accounting for taste. Or is there? American culture is a confusing amalgam of contradictions. And these contradictions are reflected not only by the movies themselves, but also by the movie industry. As Jack Nicholson once observed about the Motion Picture Association of America's rating system, "If you kiss a tit you end up with an 'R,' but if you chop one off with a sword you get a 'PG-13.'" Americans express more outrage over gay marriage than they do over the fact that millions of people in this country, most of them children, go to sleep hungry every night. Some 77 percent of Americans are Christian, a religion that allegedly eschews pornography, yet somehow the porn industry makes more money each year than all other forms of entertainment *combined*. (How is this possible *without* the contributions of the "Christian" dollar?)

Paris Hilton is a celebrity.

Given all these contradictions, what can be said of the future of Hollywood? If history is any indicator, the movie industry will continue to ebb and flow, to be primarily a factory producing formulaic, dumbed-down entertainment—but one that will also, from time to time, manage to produce movies of astonishing quality.

The hope for the movie industry is finally in the hands of writers. Without the story, without the screenplay, there is nothing but empty sound stages and actors with nothing to say or do. In his essay, Almond relates how his uncle, a movie producer, told him his book would be reduced to clichés if he sold it to Hollywood. That may be true. But a lot of high-quality movies have been adapted from short stories by Hollywood filmmakers (*Brokeback Mountain, In the Bedroom, Smoke, The Swimmer, American Splendor, Field of Dreams, Memento,* to name a few). Occasionally, even mediocre books become great films (*Midnight Cowboy, The Godfather*). Who knows what would have happened to Almond's book?

In any case, Almond might consider helping to "redeem" Hollywood, one movie at a time, by putting his considerable talent to use writing a screenplay. He could try to write a great film—one that contains some or all of the lessons he'd like us to learn—and then he could send it to Hollywood. If the script was good enough, if it was so good that turning it down would be tantamount to turning down an offer to produce, say, *Casablanca*, he could decide *not* to sell it to them unless they promise to remain faithful to his vision. He could make them an offer they couldn't refuse. I'd go see it, I can tell you that. If his movie were as entertaining as his short stories, it might even be fun.

Jerry Seinfeld's Favorite Poem

by Wendy Babiak

Jimmy Olson out-goofed Clark Kent hands down
ask any Tom, Dick or Sally at the newspaper.
Goofed-up, goofed-off, but at least his manners
seemed endless, yes ma'amming and no ma'amming Lois
holding doors while Clark stumbled into them.
And Lois with her sidelong glances at Superman
who never went unnoticed in his photogenic tights and cape
and that *S* that could have stood for *slick* or *soap*
every day saving *tout le monde* with *The Daily Planet*
serving to report it.
                    At night Jimmy dreamed
the clocks all stood still while Metropolis rocked
in waves of explosions and up in the fire-flashed sky
not a bird not a plane but Superman soared howling
with laughter, on his chest emblazoned his new letter: X.

pop flotsam. cultural jetsam.
ROCK POSTER SKETCHES

by Jay Ryan of the Bird Machine
www.thebirdmachine.com

Doc Holliday on the Importance of Comradeship: Tombstone, Arizona, October 25, 1881

by Jennifer Knox

There are two types of men in this town: trust
The one who addresses the dirt behind his ears,
Under his nails, etc. Such a man holds dear
His tether to a world beyond some mineral map.

While a dude may be the devil, I will dine
With a devil well-dressed. These boys don't know
Stink from a stampede. I believe many of them
To be in truth crafty wolf cubs that learned to walk

Upright, drink, argue, and dress—in that order—
While, ever loyal to their packs, their table manners
Remain immutably canine. If my brother were
Alive, he'd not reside in Tombstone. I could not bear

To see my own suffer under the weight of this
Flat, bone-dry dirt that might as well be the sea
In its endlessness, and us, just dumb sailors adrift—
Most cracked as a Stockton lunatic to boot.

I don't miss Christmas with the aunties, but gather
Some do, dearly. Why begrudge them their fool-hardy feuds,
Their Shakespearean spats? Indeed such squabbles
Do help time pass more quickly than solitaire.

At Noon through the Binoculars

by Jennifer Knox

We watched a gibbon
roll around in the guts
of some thing its own
size and long dead. The look
on its face! Wow: over
the moon, blissed out, high,
who cares, could die, bye bye…

Me: "What do you think?"
You: "It's remembering."
Me: "What do you think
it's remembering?"
You: "Me." Me: "You?"
You: "There are no gibbons
in this poem, only you, a fool
unschooled in the countless red
ways of the animal kingdom."

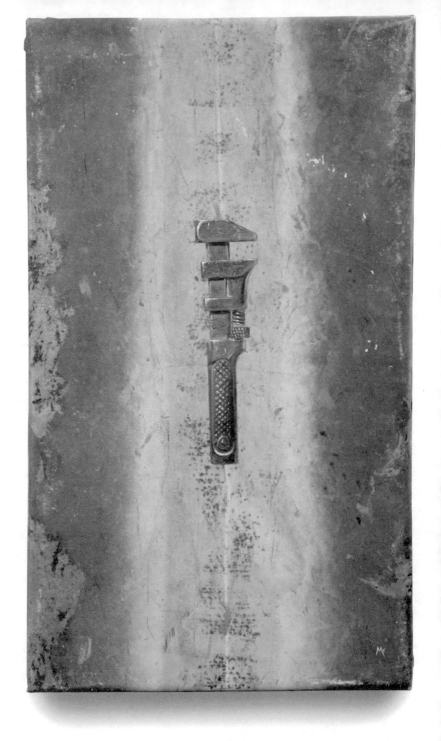

art by Mike Fitts

MARIO'S THREE LIVES BY MATT BELL

The plumber has three lives left or else he is already dead. Maybe he leaps across the gorge with ease, flying high through the air to land safely on the other side. The jump is simple because he's able to check the edge several times, waiting until he is sure of his footing, or else it's impossible, because on this world there's an invisible hand pushing him forward, speeding him along, forcing him to leap before he's ready. If that happens then the plumber is going to die. Otherwise he continues his quest, sprinting and jumping to hit blocks with his head and turtles with his ass. The blocks contain either money or food, gold coins or else mushrooms and flowers he can devour to grow bigger or stronger. Sometimes they make him fly and shoot fireballs from his fingertips. Of course, he does not actually eat anything. The closest they ever come to an orifice is when he jumps up and lands on them with his ass, just like he does to the turtles. He eats with his ass. He kills with his ass. His ass is a multi-purpose tool. Why do I have a mouth, he thinks, if I never speak or eat with it? He wonders if it's this way for everyone but there's nobody to ask. The only people he knows are the Princess, who's been abducted, and his brother, who is always missing, but who the plumber knows would carry on his quest if he should fail.

The plumber always dies with the same surprised look on his face, his mouth hanging open as he flies upward through the air before being born again at the beginning of the world. He's tiny and frightened without his mushrooms and his fireballs, desperately banging his head against blocks, looking for more. Sometimes, between reincarnations, the plumber thinks he senses God trying to decide whether to give him another chance or to just bag the whole thing. He's scared then, but who wouldn't be? He prays for continuation and then God says Continue and the music plays that means the plumber will live again. Back in the world, he realizes that the God he senses between deaths is there when he's alive too, guiding his motions. His triumphs are God's triumphs, but so are his failures. It bothers him that God can fail, but he doesn't show it. He is a stoic little plumber, looking for mushrooms and jumping on turtles. He is not a philosopher, or at least not until after the Princess is safe and he has the time to think things through. Still, sometimes when he's alive and running or, heaven forbid, swimming, he realizes that the God Who Continues is possibly not the only god there is. Surely, that god isn't the one who put all the collapsing platforms and strange, angry wildlife everywhere. At first he thinks it's the Turtle King, the one who captured the Princess and started him on this whole adventure, but then he thinks, who made the Turtle King? Not God, or at least not his god. Does this prove the existence of the devil? He doesn't know.

The plumber stomps the tiny mushroom-headed foes who wobble towards him, trying to kill him but succeeding only if he's completely careless. He bounces from one head to another, crushing a whole troop of them without touching the ground once. He is an efficient weapon, and these lowliest of enemies are no more than an inconvenience. Crawling through a maze of green pipes, the plumber realizes that he doesn't believe the devil made the turtles or their king, because that would mean the devil also made the world, and that he will not accept. He hopes he is on the side of good and decides that he must be. He is on a quest to save the Princess, and surely that is a good thing.

Now there is snow covering the land, so he slips and slides precariously down hills toward open crevasses. He springs into the air and bounces off a winged turtle to reach a higher cliff, slipping across the icy landscape. There is money everywhere, and although he picks up as much as he can, it never gets too heavy. This is because it is constantly disappearing from his pockets, going who knows where. All the plumber knows is that when he's found a lot of gold it makes it easier to come back after he falls down a pit or gets hit by some spiky creature thrown from the sky. The more money he finds, the less he ends up in the Place Where One Waits Between Continues. He hates that place, with its tense anticipation, and so he looks everywhere for gold coins or else green mushrooms, which both make the same music and have the same life-giving effect.

Finally, he sees the castle in the distance. He's passed several fake ones on his way here, convincing replicas built on other worlds, but he knows that this is the real deal. The Princess is there and so is the Turtle King. He enters.

The plumber leaps across lava and disintegrating paths. He ducks under spikes falling from ceilings and kills every enemy in his path. His mouth, his stupid useless mouth, is smiling. Soon he will save the Princess. He eats a red mushroom and turns into a giant. He eats a flower and breathes fire. The Turtle King must not defeat him. The music plays and the final fight begins, but the plumber cannot win. He dies until he runs out of lives and then he waits for God to say Continue. He waits for a long time and so he knows that God is frustrated with him. He wants to say, you're the one controlling me. It's your fault too. Give me one more chance, he prays, and I will do exactly as you say. I will jump when you say jump. I will run when you say run. I will hit anyone with my ass that you want me to hit. Please, just say the word and I shall be yours. God ponders and then says Continue, or else he doesn't. The plumber saves the Princess, or else the Turtle King conquers everything. There is no way of knowing what God will do until the moment he does it. He prays and prays. It's all any plumber can do.

Returning

by Sandra Kohler

The first heron after
Norway, stick skinny,
gawky, abrupt—
a young one? ducks, dips
into water, fishing,
then steps awkwardly,
jauntily into a different
river.

       ***

Two pairs of geese
on the river: one
followed by one gosling,
the other, a string of
twenty-some tiny swimmers.
The house that burned
before we left is still
standing, half-raised,
the house that was
being built is not yet
finished.

       ***

Norwegian light:
so clear, cruel. Looking
into the mirror on our last
day, the weather wrinkled
face of all the old women
I've seen on the journey,

every line revealed
by that light clear
and brutal as
eternity.

***

Flying home, I
imagine writing a history
of my siblings, their past
and present relations, as if
the mind, a sea away, saw
pattern in an intricate
braided web. Home,
I realize what you see
is what you get:
a sea, a cloud of
unknowing.

***

Yesterday's heron
seemed herald, token:
pillar of fire, pillar
of cloud. This morning,
the wilderness is itself
again. All I know
is what not to
expect.

The Flat Land

by Kate Lovelady

I made a pilgrimage to a field of sorrow,
expecting the skeletal frame of a house
with no future, a garden lying fallow.
He should be gone. Without an heir what use

is building? But fresh joists gleam like wounds
beneath a cheerful yellow tarp, and black crows
court and chase over newly furrowed ground
that sports not grass but leeks and fleshy tomatoes.

Beyond this scene, hidden by the modest trees,
a rough stone as their monument, her ashes
hide alone in their box. He wouldn't see
them scattered: "I want to know where my daughter is."

My hands recall the plastic cube, grass green
and heavy as a thousand-page book,
onionskin heavy as a beam. . . .
                              All the boughs should break.

The birds should fall
Silent. The crickets stop calling, everything
should stop. And then my heart.

Hammering.   He's back at work. Singing.

How could he?
            I set a candle by the stone
and prop two scraps of bark to block the wind;
a piece of quartz-flecked flint. A clump
of moss completes a glowing shelter.

Carl's singing "Summertime." How
Anne hated musicals.

Grief is the flat land

where we build homes
and live. Just beyond the reaching shadows
the rising frame is burnished orange. I can't
see Carl quite yet, though I can hear his hammer,
            steady in the ribs.

art by Cecelia Ferriera

Barrelhouse

ME CHIP
by David Barringer

My daughter stayed home from school because her MeChip was malfunctioning. The
repairman was due before lunch. My daughter was in bed. She'd been
having bad dreams for six nights. Her screams—the physical conjuring
of them, the sound of them in her head, her ribcage and diaphragm
contracting to produce and sustain them—none of it was enough to
wake her up. The nightmare had seized her from within and she couldn't
shake loose. We'd dash into her room and see her sitting upright in bed,
once even standing up, and her eyes were closed and her hair was sweaty
and lay wet on her face, streams of dark wet lines on her forehead and
temples and down her cheeks and crawling down the back of her neck
like someone had drawn thick black lines downward from her skull,
tentacles squeezing her head. We held her and wiped her face and felt
the hot seizures of her facial muscles. We whispered and cooed. She bit
my wife on the neck. She punched me in the Adam's apple, and I had to
inhale through my nose and cough as hard as I could to start breathing
again. When I was my daughter's age, a babysitter taught me how to
disable an attacker by thumbing him in the throat, by cracking the car-
tilage of the Adam's apple. It seemed I was a stand-in for my daughter's
attacker, and I was disabled.

For the last three days, Lilly had slept in our bed, but the dreams
kept coming. Tina and I planned to take turns sleeping downstairs on
the couch, but neither of us could continue to sleep once Lilly's screams
erupted, tearing holes in the night and boiling us in our fears: a burglar,
a fallen bookcase, a fire. We had nothing to do for her but be there.

It wasn't until breakfast on the fifth day, when I was singing and dancing like an operatic ape, wired and sleep deprived and fighting her anxiety with vaudevillian slapstick, that Lilly said, "You're just the dad I needed," dropped her cereal spoon to the floor, and, reaching for it, fell off her chair as if in playful imitation of the spoon. I picked her up, and she said she couldn't feel her arm. She couldn't feel any of it. She couldn't make it move. I pinched her arm once, then twice, harder, and she watched and said, "Am I dying?"

Our community of Stratford, Michigan, was one of three small towns chosen, from hundreds of willing candidates, for MeChip's pilot program. All three towns shared a single compelling burden: Civil services were overtaxed by a flood of new suburbanites. The small towns couldn't accommodate so many new residents. The towns' tax bases had been contracting for twenty years from the loss of auto-factory jobs, and the available land was quickly being developed into subdivisions for commuters. It was hoped that the pilot program might alleviate this burden and ease the growing pains of overwhelmed communities.

The MeChip was an I.D. chip, a locator chip. While it wasn't mandatory for schoolkids, those parents who opted out of the MeChip program were assessed higher local taxes for fire, police, and school. The theory was that it cost more to rescue, track down, and monitor non-MeChip kids than MeChip kids. A burning home. Firefighter scans for MeChips, locates one, raises a no-nonsense ladder to the second-floor window for a precise extraction. For non-MeChip kids, it's guesswork. Ladder goes up to whatever window's available, firefighter wanders around the house, risks life and limb, and maybe there aren't any kids in there anyway. Kidnapping. Witnesses report a blue sedan, a light-blue minivan. Which is it? Which way did it go? Police scramble. Parents break down, plead into television cameras. Dad cleans the .357 in the basement, loads it, and drives around town looking for a blue sedan, a light-blue minivan. He dreams of vengeance and plans to adopt a calm, cool, yet grief-stricken demeanor to present to the prosecutor, the judge, the jury. *Who would have thought my life would have taken such a turn? Of course, I killed him. I am a parent. This is my world. A madman may enter, but he will not leave.* Or. Scan the county for the MeChip kid, send two patrol cars to 666 Inferno Drive, bust down the door, two headshots to the perp one-legging it out the bathroom window, wrap

MeChip kid #544-01-3392 in a green police blanket, carry her out the front door to the on-air lights of Channels 2, 4, 7, 50, and 62, and you've got weepy parents, relieved communities, and restored faith in law and order, all with an affordable price, timely delivery, and minimal risk to human life.

As a family, we balanced costs and benefits. The cost of the home implantation kit and the monthly MeChip security service turned out to be greater, not less, than the higher taxes and state assessment fees. If non-MeChip kids were more expensive for city services to deal with, then why was it cheaper to *opt out* of the MeChip program? With the MeChip, we gained something we could not have had under the alternative: increased security for our children, and peace of mind. We did it for our children.

"It's for you," I thought as I shot the implantation needle into Lilly's arm and she whelped in pain. It had to be done. She'd be safe now. (Unless the kidnappers wised up and lopped off MeChip limbs and in general speeded up their tortures in anticipation of the swifter deployment of technology-enhanced justice.)

Lilly bawled and bawled on her white sleigh bed in her Easter-pink bedroom where we thought she'd feel safest, and I couldn't bear to think that what I had done to her, the pain I was putting her through, wasn't going to be worth it. Blood trickled down her arm. She palmed her wound and rocked back and forth and Tina comforted her with hugs and persuaded Lilly to release her grip. Tina disinfected the area with a spray can and blew on the pink skin still marked with Lilly's tight palmprint over the raised welt of the implantation site. Tina wiped the blood from Lilly's hand and the tears from her cheeks and said, "It's okay, honey. It's over. You did great. We're so proud of you."

I retreated to the instruction manual and followed the steps for proper disposal of the implantation needle and MeChip cartridge, which were to be sealed in a black plastic bag, included with the kit, and not trashed curbside but, instead, packaged with our completed forms and Lilly's information, and all of it mailed to their address in a plain brown cardboard box, which they would process and catalog and retain for monitoring purposes whenever in the future the need should arise to track Lilly down via the MeChip shot into her right bicep. I needed to test the MeChip right away, according to the manual. So I went through the test procedure with the disposable MeChip scanner and GPS. I saw my daughter as a red blinking light on the screen, and the readout gave latitude and longitude and street address, and if I touched my fingernail to her blinking light I could zoom in on her location until a white-line rendering of our house appeared and Lilly blinked in the second-story bedroom, northeast.

I clicked "Yes" in answer to whether the test was successful, which seemed odd to me, a solicitation of my subjective interpretation of what had just happened. What I wanted was an objective conclusion from this little dealie, assuring me that what had just happened was what happens when a test is successful. If I knew more than the machine, for crying out loud…but, then again, I was pleased to learn an awareness of fallibility was built into the system. This was a responsible company, I thought. And I knew I was meant to think this. I surrendered to this smug outfit my money, but I withheld my trust, which amounted to psychological resistance, about which they cared zip as long as I paid my monthly service charge and didn't clamor at City Hall for a competitive open-bid process in the hopes of driving down prices and driving up quality and service. I shipped off the box.

In less than a day, Lilly healed strong and whole.

The next month, Tina brought down the bill and asked, "It's worth it, right? I mean, I know it is. I just—I mean, Trey, look at this. The money, wow."

And I said, "Yeah, but you never want to find out if it's worth it, you know?"

And Tina said, "I worry about her as much as I always have. I worry something's gonna happen, and will this damn thing work, and if it doesn't and it's back to the old way, then what's the point? And what do we do then, get a refund? We don't want a refund. We want Lilly."

And I said, "We'll worry about her until the day we die. No way to get around that."

And Tina said, "We could take this money and send her to a private school. That's something to consider. Maybe there are other ways. There's gotta be other ways."

And I said, "I'm sure a private school is more expensive than this, and they'd probably have a similar kind of MeChip deal. They'd probably have something even more expensive."

Tina held a porcelain cup under the water dispenser and said, "Tea," into the speaker. Inhaling herbal steam as boiling water filled her cup, she turned and asked, "You want any?"

That night, about a month after implantation, Lilly had her first nightmare.

After breakfast on the fifth day, the morning Lilly's arm went numb, I called the MeChip hotline and was directed to maintenance. They scheduled a home visit for the next day.

The repairman arrived about an hour after lunch. He was late. I wasn't surprised. Lilly was on the couch watching TV, and the repairman said she could keep on watching while he ran the tests. He moved handheld devices over Lilly's arm and took readings of the MeChip. I stood and watched him do his repairman thing and watched Lilly peek and flinch; obviously she was no longer able to relax and watch TV. Why should she trust this man, this MeChip, this cause of her nightly torment?

"It's broken," he said, bagging his tools. He seemed a cross between a doctor and an electrician.

"We figured that," I said.

And he said, "Can't fix it. Gotta take it out."

He was heading for the door as if to leave, and I said, "So you need something from the truck to take it out?"

And he said, "Nope. Can't do that. You gotta do it." He unzipped a side pocket of his bag and pulled out a slip of paper and said, "Order this. Takes two weeks. Home removal kit."

I asked him didn't he have one in the truck, and he said no, only the parent is authorized, and I asked, "So you disabled it, right? I mean, her arm was numb, and the dreams. That stuff's over, right? The thing's turned off?"

And he said, "Can't turn it off. Doesn't work like that," and left.

I kicked the door shut.

Lilly stayed home doing her homework in bed, writing with her left hand, and suffering the symptoms of a screwed-up MeChip. I joined other parents in suing for emotional distress and physical damage, arguing this kind of suffering is what the MeChip is supposed to fucking prevent, not cause.

The removal kit arrived. Only took a week.

Again, Tina and I headed up to Lilly's bedroom, where we believed she would feel safest. Tina wrapped her in the teal comforter and got in bed behind her. They looked like bobsledders in that white sleigh bed. I wanted to prepare myself for the pain I was going to put Lilly through, again. This time, probably worse. A larger cut. A bloody uprooting of some alien metallic infestation. I followed the instructions. I wrapped what resembled a blood-pressure cuff around her arm. Lilly was already crying. Tina was rocking back and forth with her.

"Let's think of a story to tell," Tina said.

"No, no," Lilly said, talking to me, not Tina. Lilly's focus was on me. On what I was about to do to her and what I was about to do it with.

I didn't blame her. I hated this, too. I was relieved to see the fire in Lilly's eyes. I wanted her to fight back. Wasn't that what a parent should inspire in his child: a fighting spirit? an unyielding will?

Tina told a story about a young girl who was Lilly's age, and she had a big performance coming up. She'd been practicing for such a long time, but there was one movement she still couldn't master. She wanted more than anything to learn it. What could she do? Who would help her?

That was as much as I heard because Lilly was distracted by the story, and I moved on quickly to the next step. I pressed a button. A cord connected the cuff to a small box the size of a video-game console. I waited while the machine hummed and the cuff inflated and throbbed and hummed along with the machine. I listened for Tina's story, but she was speaking it into Lilly's ear. Watching them, I had one of those fatherly feelings, possessive yet isolating. They were sharing an intimate moment, and I was fooling with machinery. We were connected but on opposite ends. They were aligned against me, and that was okay. I could be the bad guy—the bad guy who thought he was the good guy. I felt abiding tenderness towards my wife and daughter, tenderness that transcended the moment and made me look on them with a million-year Milky Way stare. Still, I resented them a little. Mother and Daughter had withdrawn into a secret alliance, warming themselves beneath a synthetic down comforter, while Father stood guard outside in the cold, smoking an organic cigarette under a mercury-vapor lamp, stomping to keep warm, turning his back against whirling drifts of snow imported from Russia....Funny, the associations a restless mind makes, the vain indulgences of a wounded heart. But the mind can be its own savior. I understood my emotions were real, but they were petty; so I snubbed them out, flicking them into the Russian snow and crushing them with my landowner's boots, judging them childish and beneath me. Here was my wife and daughter, in this room, in our home, the only citizens in our own private country. And here I was, too. We worked hard to get here, very hard, and we had to stop *ourselves* from spoiling it. And so I paid attention to the small and temporary, and felt the large and timeless, and fought the meanness in me day by day, moment by moment. Our family fought not to survive but to stay strong enough to wonder, each day, how to live well. And we were not satisfied with sitting in front of the entertainment wall and wondering about the good life. We got up and turned into the wind and damn well tried to make it happen.

They were sharing an intimate moment, and I was fooling with machinery. We were connected but on opposite ends.

Then the machine clicked off. It stopped. That was it?

I reread the manual.

Huh. That was it. The MeChip just dissolved. It would be eaten up by white blood cells or passed through the body or I didn't know what. The language wasn't clear.

"My arm tingles," said Lilly.

And that night she had no bad dreams.

A couple weeks later, the envelope arrived. The monthly bill. We weren't charged for the removal kit. Instead, we were invited to a town meeting to be held at City Hall in one week.

We attended.

At the meeting, we were informed that the MeChip product, now discontinued, was being replaced with nanotechnology embedded in a hair or hairs. A single hair was enough to provide a tracking signal, but a child could be host to many hairs, all with the same I.D. number.

"Nanohair," the presenter explained, "is easy to wear and falls out after three months and needs to be replaced. Kind of like disposable contact lenses. Nanohair is safer, more hygienic, and the bad guys can't tell which hair to remove."

Under my breath, I whispered to those around me, "And they won't be tempted to lop off a limb." Then I got another thought and decided to speak up about it. "The kidnappers," I said, "wouldn't they just shave the kid?"

The parents in the room drew a collective breath and waited for what they knew would come: the bullshit. At the start of the meeting, the parents were invited to give feedback and vent about the bad MeChips previously recalled. Parents of children who'd suffered from malfunctioning MeChips had joined forces in a class-action lawsuit against the manufacturer. We'd settled for an amount of money we knew they'd get back out of us one way or another, through taxes or new monthly service charges for, say, Nanohair. So the parents at this meeting were realists, skeptics, tough customers. We'd been made this way.

The presenters hadn't thought to ask the Nanohair inventors about shaving. But they were experienced in public relations, thought quickly, and said, "Look, something has to be done for the children, and this is a real improvement. We're constantly innovating new solutions. Your feedback is welcome and encouraged. We can work together to protect our children the best way we can."

And they should have left it at that. But another presenter, one with a practical mind and an impractical conscience, pointed out that shaving was a difficult if not impossible way to remove the Nanohair, and shaving was, anyway, less violent than the previous anti-MeChip scenarios.

Parents were sitting in fold-out chairs, backed by an American flag, fronted by a dais and a committee of civic representatives involved in the security program, and every one of them—every parent in City Hall—was imagining a madman shaving their child. Their child was squirming. A tangle of limbs in a motel bathtub. Shrieks and whimpers. The madman was making nicks and cuts over the child's body, each square inch of skin scraped at with a razor, a cheap disposable razor, because no one could picture a madman with an expensive razor, an electric razor. And then there was the head hair, the shaving of the skull, the blood running into the eyes and into the ears. And then the shaving of the eyebrows and the eyelashes and, yes, every crevice and crotch of the child's body.

"Could they use bleach or acid?" Tina asked.

Half the people in the room were standing. Tina let go of my hand and stood with them. Her standing up displaced a body of air that felt warm on my face and smelled of deodorant and the Kate Spade perfume I'd bought her. I hesitated. Tina was wearing dark slacks that I'd helped de-lint with the sticky roller before we came to the meeting. I brushed my knuckles against the fabric and then palmed the rounded metal sides of my chair as if to get up, but I didn't yet. The presenters were upset by the disruption. One hurried out into a hallway and didn't return. Committee members rose from their side of the table and waved to calm us down. Unbuttoned suitcoats flapped like wings under their raised arms. White sleeve cuffs were exposed. They were like office workers unused to labor waving self-importantly at a truck to signal the delivery could not be made here. At City Hall, they were signaling that the show would not go on unless decorum was maintained. But I wondered if they underestimated the parents. For the parents, the show would not go on unless questions were answered. I stood up and took my wife's hand in my own. I supposed we were acting on behalf of the children. Tina was shouting to be heard. "Could they burn the hair off?"

We were all thinking like madmen now. We were all shaving our children, burning the hair off their skin, considering the logistics of it, walking through it step by step, from beginning to end, and there seemed to be no way to stop it. No way to look at our children without shame. No way to take them into our arms and protect them through the night and shield them through the day. No way to let them be children again, to be ourselves again—no way except the way it had to be done. The way we would do it. The way we had to do it. MeChips. Nanohair. We had done it before. We would do it again.

Chairs clattered and collapsed like metal dominoes.

Parents surged forward with practical questions.

The faces of the committee were boiled and white.
"Wait!" I cried.
We would do it for our children.

pop flotsam. cultural jetsam.

ROCK POSTER SKETCHES

by Jay Ryan of the Bird Machine
www.thebirdmachine.com

art by Mike Fitts

Kinda Saving Myself for the Scene:
Barrelhousing with the Hold Steady

The Hold Steady make rock music that's equally suitable for back seat headbanging and coffee house reading. And I don't mean reading the *New Yorker* while listening to the Hold Steady on your iPod – I mean actually reading the lyrics. Led by singer and songwriter Craig Finn, Hold Steady songs read like Denis Johnson short stories, cooked with spoon over lighter, perhaps, until they've been boiled down to their essence. That's why it's fitting that, despite how much I'd eventually appreciate their music, I first read The Hold Steady instead of listening to them. In March 2005, I came across the early MP3 blog The Big Ticket, where I read a post containing partial lyrics to the song "Most People are DJs:"

I was a teenage ice machine
I kept it cool in coolers & I drank until I dreamed
When I dreamed, I always dreamed about the scene
All these kids look like little lambs looking up at me
I was a Twin Cities trash bin, I did everything they'd give me
I'd jam it into my system
She got me cornered in by kitchen, I said I'll do anything but listen
To some weird talking chick who just can't understand
That we're hot soft spots on a hard rock planet

Baby take off your beret
Everyone's a critic & most people are DJs
And everything gets played

A thousand kids will fall in love in all these clubs tonight
A thousand other kids will end up gushing blood tonight
Two thousand kids won't get all that much sleep tonight
Two thousand kids they still feel pretty sweet tonight
Yeah, I still feel pretty sweet

I went out that same day and bought that album, their 2004 outing *The Hold Steady Almost Killed Me*, which was just as I'd hoped: filled with gritty lyrics, vivid imagery, and a sense of humor. I played *Almost Killed Me* nonstop until late 2005, when their *Separation Sunday* was released. Through singer Finn's spectacular lyrics, *Separation Sunday* told the story of Holly (aka Halleluiah), an addict, prostitute, and sometimes born again Christian, and her interactions with a pimp named Charlemagne and another man named Gideon as they travel from city to city, all three of them getting high, sobering up, finding Jesus, and falling in and out of love and life. *Separation Sunday* showcased for the first time what would become the permanent band behind him: founding guitarist Tad Kulbert, Franz Nicolay on keyboards, Galen Polivka on bass, and Bobby Drake on drums.

In 2006, The Hold Steady released their third and most accomplished album to date, *Boys and Girls in America*. Named from a quote from Jack Kerouac's *On The Road* ("boys and girls in America have such a sad time together"), it is a theme album about teenage relationships, in all their glory, all their confusion. Lyrically, the album both continues Finn's regional focus on Minneapolis's indie rock scene while at the same time expanding into new lyrical and musical territory.

I talked to Craig Finn and Tad Kulbert in late 2006, soon after they arrived home to Brooklyn after touring coast to coast in support of *Boys and Girls in America*. We talked about the new album, their recent tour, the burden of being sincere (and Catholic) in a hipster's world, Craig's plans for becoming a novelist someday, and the importance of knowing where you're from.

Matt Bell: First *Almost Killed Me*, and then *Separation Sunday*, and now *Boys and Girls in America*. It's been a great couple years for you guys—I'm not sure anyone has released a better three albums in three years in a long time.

Craig Finn: Thank you—I'm not sure you're right, but I appreciate it. As for releasing three albums that fast, that was by design. When I formed the Hold Steady, I said, We're the kind of band that's going to put out a record every year. That said, I don't think we'll actually be able to put one out in 2007, as much as it's going to kill me not to.

MB: Your lyrics are obviously a big part of what people like about the band, and certainly what initially drew me to The Hold Steady. The first thing I heard was "Most People are DJs" back when *Almost Killed Me* first came out, which is full of these fantastic images. From the new album, one that sticks out is "You Can Make Like You"—"you can wear his old sweatshirt/you can cover yourself like a bruise"—or last album's "she crashed into the Easter mass with her hair done up in broken glass." Do you have central images that you start writing your songs from? Where's your starting point as a lyricist?

CF: Going back to *Separation Sunday*, I had notes pasted all over my wall. You know, arrows pointing to this and that. It was a story. The new one is more of a theme album, rather than a concept one. I took that line out of Kerouac, not just "boys and girls in America have such a sad time together" but the rest of it too—"sophistication demands that they submit to sex immediately without proper preliminary talk"—not courtship, but real talk about souls—I taped that to the wall, and every time I got stuck I just stared at that.

MB: When I was preparing for this interview, I went back and got *On The Road* off the shelf. It's been about five years, and I just read that one chapter, but it occurs to me that the whole thing reads like a Hold Steady song. The scene with the girl, and everyone's leaving town because it's sort of crap, but he's still going to come back sometime and see what else is going on…

CF: *On The Road* is really incredible. It's my father's favorite book, so when I was sixteen I read it, and I was a real asshole about it. I didn't understand it. It's funny, because when I reread it there was nothing that was over my head when I was sixteen, I just didn't have the experience for it. I didn't miss the concepts, but I did miss the humor. When I reread it, I laughed on almost every page. At least one sentence per page, he just nailed something.

What I hope, even though I know I'm not doing it as well as Kerouac, is that I'm explaining these things specifically. What Kerouac does is he tells you somehow, by explaining what he himself is doing, he tells you something about America, and I think that that's the interesting thing.

MB: That ambition definitely comes through on the album. You compare it to the focus on Holly's story you have in *Separation Sunday*, and now you're taking a much wider approach, coming at the same thing from a multitude of angles.

CF: One thing that's always been a central theme for me—You know, people always ask me what's up with all the stuff about Minneapolis. One of the reasons I do that is that I can, that I know Minneapolis. If you tell me a situation, I can probably tell you what block it happened on. In this day and age, we tour around, there's Home Depot everywhere, there's the Gap, there's Urban Outfitters. You say something specific from someone's town, people go fucking nuts. When Kerouac, when he goes to Denver—It's like a western town, like somewhere he's never been before. Like fucking cowboys. Now, you go to Denver it's not that different from Minneapolis or Baltimore.

MB: And that holds true for any city in America now.

CF: That why's I think using these specific places and people to explain something more widely experienced is a big part of what I'm trying to do.

MB: There was a quote in Pitchfork from a show of yours in New York, relating to place, where you said, "Wherever you're from…" I thought that really just seemed to tie into your Minneapolis stories and your writing about those locales.

CF: I think it affects me more now that I've moved to New York, where I know all these people who've also moved to New York from other cities, and now New York is their identity. I end up being embarrassed by them, because they don't fool anyone, and also because moving to a city in America is just an option, you know? It doesn't mean anything. I guess because I'm hyper aware of that, I don't want to be that guy. New York hasn't become part of my identity.

MB: I've only visited New York, and I'm from a pretty small town and moved to a pretty small city in the Midwest. New York is overwhelming when I'm there, but I can definitely see the appeal.

CF: I love it, but I still just think it's really important to remember where you're from.

MB: You don't arrive in Brooklyn and become a different person.

CF: Right. At the same time, I look back now, and here's something that shaped my life: When I was a young teenager, my parents announced we were moving. We had lived in Boston, and my parents tell me that dad's got a job in Minneapolis and that we're moving there. Five years later, I get into music, and there's the Replacements and Hüsker Dü, and I got to see them play in front of 200 people. I wonder if I'd even be in a band right now if my parents had moved to, you know, Chicago or Houston instead of Minneapolis. Because in Minneapolis music is such a part of the culture. It's really weird. I feel like, for instance, if you go to a show, there's all kinds of dudes there who wouldn't be there if they lived in any other city. They want to get girls, and girls are at the shows. It's just part of the social thing in Minneapolis. I don't know how to explain it, but it's a very musical town.

The city grew a lot in the seventies, early eighties, and the people moving there were from out east and they wanted to make the city like their old cities. There was a lot of money going to the arts, etc. The other thing is that right now Minneapolis is just a mature scene. The Replacements happened in '82, '83, then Hüsker Dü in '84, and in the last twenty years music has become a real important part of the city.

MB: Obviously, this album has it's Jack Kerouac influences, but what other writers mean a lot to your work?

CF: You know, I get asked this a lot, but...OK, here's an example. Recently, I did an interview with Colin Meloy. This Canadian magazine put us together, and I'll tell you what—people are always saying in articles about us, "Craig Finn's very literary," but Colin Meloy is literary, Craig Finn is not. That dude's read fifteen books for every one I've read.

MB: I think he has songs that are based on three different books, like it takes a thousand pages of literature to make a three-minute song.

CF: Exactly. I mean, I read pulp. The guy who interviewed us thought we'd go well together because we were both supposedly literary people, but I keep going, "Well, I just heard what Colin said so now I'm afraid to talk."

MB: Any plans to expand your writing, to write short stories or novels? Obviously, lyrically, you're one of my favorite writers, but you write songs, not stories, so that's a little odd for me.

CF: I've got a novel, or at least a novel I want to write. All I have is an outline, and I keep expanding it. I figure in forty years I'll have enough outlined it'll just write itself. I just haven't put pen to paper. I have the story, and I think it's really good. That's all I can really say about it.

MB: We'll just have to look forward to it in the future then.

CF: It's kind of a mystery, but not a detective one. Ah, what the hell, I'll tell you this too. It takes place regarding a specific crime that really happens in Minneapolis.

MB: It does seem like by default anything you write would be set in Minneapolis at least as a starting place.

CF: I thought about all the cities in America, and somehow came upon the town of Minneapolis sort of randomly.

MB: I'm sure that's exactly the way it happened.

CF: I really think I'm giving people the wrong idea about Minneapolis with my music. When people who only know Minneapolis through my music go there for the first time, they're always surprised. They're like, "Hey, Minneapolis is nice. You don't make it sound so nice."

MB: You know, it really seems *Boys and Girls in America* has a lot of great moments, changes in mood. It's definitely more positive in places—"Massive Nights," for instance—than *Separation Sunday* was. Beyond Kerouac, what other influences informed the album?

CF: One of the main influences on *Boys and Girls in America* was listening to *Separation Sunday* critically. I have this friend who's really smart and I really value her opinion, and she said to me, "I loved *Almost Killed Me* and I can never listen to *Separation Sunday* because it was too awful, too dark." I personally think it's really hopeful, but I'm obviously not doing my job well enough if someone that I really respect can't get that.

Also, when I listened to it more, I sort of felt like it was an Oliver Stone movie. There's one point and it keeps banging your head against it. I decided I wanted to make an Ang Lee album. *Boys and Girls in America* is twice as deep, but it might take people longer to get all of it. It's way more subtle.

The other thing about *Separation Sunday* is that when you're dealing with indie rockers, taking a Catholic position on anything, is so removed from anything they think that a certain number of people got a head trip just off of that. To me, I just grew up with it so it was natural to write about.

MB: I was raised Catholic so I think that's one of the reasons I identified with it. These are the things I grew up with as well.

CF: So you know what I mean then. I don't go to church anymore, but I'm still a Catholic, just because I spent so much of my life there. I went to Boston College, I went to Catholic school, and I believe it. It informs me. It's a very important part of my life, but you deal with indie rockers or artists and all you get is "Catholic priests are child molesters."

MB: I was at the Detroit show a couple weeks ago, and also at the one two years ago. Maybe it's just me, but I tend to focus on the lyrical aspects of your albums when I'm listening to them at home. Seeing you perform live tends to highlight other aspects instead, such as the guitar solos or Franz's keyboarding, which I then take back to my listening at home. All the albums are better once you've heard them live.

Tad Kulbert: I think that in essence, being a touring rock and roll band, that's what we do. I think the fun that we have doing this is real contagious. One thing I always hear from people who've seen our shows, people who like our band and also people doing interviews, is that there's no disconnect between the stage and the audience. It's sometimes impossible to discern where one begins and one ends. I think that everyone really feels a part of the celebration and of rock and roll. If you're going to take it to that level, well, I did our last four shows with what my doctor still thinks might be a broken ankle, but I just can't not go up and there and give one hundred percent. That's what we do, and that's what makes it fun for us.

MB: Obviously, one of the ways *Boys and Girls in America* differs from *Separation Sunday* is that it's more thematically organized rather than conceptually or as a continuous story. Are there other differences in the writing that helped make this album so different? For instance, Tad, I understand that you have a two year-old daughter, and that "Citrus" started out as something you played for her.

TK: One of the things going into this record is that I wanted it be a little more dynamic, guitar-wise. I wanted to try and do different stuff, and finger-picking is not something I'm super strong at. I was listening to a lot of Nick Drake and Elliot Smith and Willie Nelson, and so I decided to make up some exercises to practice, and that kind of morphed into that song. So I played it for her all the time, which is fun because she's fascinated with playing the guitar. She just focuses. I showed it to Craig, and I kind of knew what the record was going to be about lyrically, the theme that he wanted to bring to the record—not really a concept, but just that he wanted it to be about relationships. Had I not known that, I might not have brought a song like that in. Eventually he and I sat down and hammered it out in about half an hour.

MB: I think the music has really grown from *Almost Killed Me*, where it felt like more of a backdrop for Craig, to *Separation Sunday*, where the music got much more complex. *Boys and Girls in America* is, for me, the album where the music and the lyrics finally feel inseparable from each other.

CF: I feel really lucky—the band's really good. I don't write any of the music, just the lyrics. Tad's my favorite guitar player, and I just happen to be in a band with him. He's a monster. You go to shows every night and you won't see another guitarist who plays like him.

TK: A lot of the growth can be attributed to Franz coming on board. On the last record, I'd written the majority of the record when he actually joined the band. On this one, when I came up with ideas, he and I would sit down with a piano and a guitar and try to really create them so they worked together. Franz is a great musician, and the caliber of musicianship with that guy is just incredible. I wanted to be sure that we really kind of let him run. He brought a lot to the table—it's like a music lesson every time we sit down together. I studied theory in college, but he's got a degree in jazz composition, and I think he really brought us to a new level. Bobby also was our previous touring drummer and officially joined the band right before *Separation Sunday*, where on this album he was real comfortable with voicing his opinion and bringing ideas from the beginning. Our rhythm section is such an important part of the band—Galen is one of the best bass players around, in terms of subtlety and playing ability.

MB: One of the overarching connections that makes your music so engaging to me is that your songs often celebrate that part of your life you're not supposed to celebrate after a certain age, as well as a style of music you're not supposed to enjoy anymore, especially if you're an indie rock hipster. You're not supposed to look back and be excited about your drugged out, sex-crazed teenage years, and you're not supposed to be overly enthused about classic rock.

CF: I think those two do go together, obviously. For me, the classic rock thing, well, I was a punk rocker, but before Kurt Cobain there was no alt rock radio. So once you got in your car, in Minneapolis you listened to KQRF, the only rock station, and they played the Eagles and the Stones. So you could be a punk rocker, but you had your favorite Who songs too, and there was really no shame in it, because it wasn't like you were choosing that over Black Flag, it's just what was available in the car, and you lived with it. I think it's kind of good, because it forced you to listen to things you might not have. Otherwise you might just listen to your favorite band over and over again.

MB: Well, I don't want to take up any more of your time, but I do have to ask you guys one more question.

CF: Go ahead, shoot.

TK: Anything.

MB: Barrelhouse has a slight fixation on Patrick Swayze, and so the final question of every interview is this: What's your favorite Patrick Swayze film?

TK: Seriously?

MB: Yeah. Ian McKaye almost punched someone in the face over it, as I understand it.

CF: *Road House.* How could it not be?

TK: [Long pause] I'm going to say *The Outsiders*.

MB: Great choice. Thank you very—

TK: Actually, you know what? I'll give you my top three: *Outsiders*, *Red Dawn*, and, for the quote alone—"Nobody puts Baby in the corner"—*Dirty Dancing*.

pop flotsam. cultural jetsam.
ROCK POSTER SKETCHES

by Jay Ryan of the Bird Machine
www.thebirdmachine.com

Our Love Poems Are in Janis Joplin's Stockpot

by Allison McEntire

That's three times now I've seen Janis Joplin's ghost—

once in a bowling alley waffle shack smoking a stolen cigarette,
one tremulous column of ash tipped over the rim of her bowl of beef stew
like the remains of the skin that was shed by a dream—

once in the passenger side of a passing moving van,
the screeching banshee snatching fistfuls of hair from the scalp of a man
who didn't seem to notice who was doing what beside him—

and once
in our bed, with you,
my love.

Other people's wasted love poems
piss Janis Joplin off. Now that she is a shadow (the shadow of a flame,
the skinned remains of an inhaled dream) she can't stand to see
bad love poems discarded. She screams the lines we write on the folds of our
skin

then gobbles the words back up quick.
Her laughter is mechanical, like a dishwasher,
but her hunger is the licked-clean inside of an empty bowl.

.

She grubs up our rotting, unloaded sentiments,
old meat carved away from over-broiled emotion,
and pops the stock in pots she's wedged everywhere between us:

in the waffle shack behind the dishwasher,
or in the moving van, near the radio.
Here behind my pillow, there beneath your head.

She simmers up the slack words of our slick love,
singing as she skims the thick white word grease
from the top.

She's got to have that taste.

For
The Love
of Good TV
by
Melanie
Springer
Mock

art by Cecelia Ferriera

This was my summer idyll: a musty cement-blocked basement, painted yellow; an olive green couch and woolen weave rug; and a Zenith 24-inch screen on its metallic altar. Every afternoon, during the community pool's dinner break, I stretched out on the rug for a trinity of television nirvana—*The Brady Bunch*, *Gilligan's Island*, and *The Beverly Hillbillies*.

Although they were already in syndication, the shows seemed ageless to me: they were contemporaries not only of the television scene, but also of my own late-70s childhood. It almost felt as if Peter and Jan were entering groovy Filmore Junior High just as I was attending Hillsboro Middle School; and that Gilligan and the Skipper were trading barbs on their deserted island simultaneous to Jethro's nightly swims in the cement pond.

The basement, dark and cool, afforded its own kind of timelessness, just like the television shows. I could hear my mom knocking around upstairs, preparing our wholesome Mennonite supper, but I was caught in the vortex of sitcom ecstasy, and the creaking ceiling was only vague background thrum. Until 6:00, when mom hollered down the stairwell just as the final twang of the Hillbillies' theme song sounded.

My spell was broken, and I flew up the stairs to my family.

Saturday nights provided a different, potentially more lurid lineup, one I watched in furtive solitude or, on occasion, with my brother and sister. *The Love Boat* highlighted the evening's entertainment, and my crush on Gopher Smith was only occasionally trumped by the thrilling recognition of a guest star on the Princess, someone with certain prestige, like John Ritter or Robert Reed.

Meanwhile, my parents were upstairs enacting their own love boat, and if seas were not rocky, I could enjoy a full hour of *Fantasy Island*, too. That is, until the episode in which chosen Island visitors could see the future in an enchanted ring. Such fantasy proved grim when one seeker saw a car wreck, another her gravestone. Alone in the now-darkened basement, the portend of an eerie future seemed a little too much; I switched off the television and thumped up the stairs, no doubt rousing my parents from their Saturday night routine.

In Sunday school, my friends and I would dissect *The Love Boat*'s morality plays while Mrs. Lohrenz nattered uninspired about Noah or Abraham or some such. On rarest occasion, one of us could brag about also seeing *Saturday Night Live*, at 10:30 Central Time, and although of course we could little understand the show's satire, the lucky among us could at least claim to have laughed the *entire hour*.

The linoleum-floored church classroom became our own prepubescent water cooler—or, in a cultural rite more apropos to our context, a place to mull story lines much as our grandmothers did over coffee about *As the World Turns* and *The Guiding Light*. It never seemed freakishly odd that we would use Sunday school to gossip about who scored on *The Love Boat*, or whose mind was fucked by Mr. Roarke and Tattoo. It also did not seem odd—at the time—that Mennonite parents would fail to monitor their kids' watching habits and, indeed, let their kids view such naughty programming, using Captain Stubing as a weekly babysitter so they could have uninterrupted Saturday night sex.

In fact, none of my television habits seemed odd or unnatural to me, not the Saturday night Spelling orgy or the summertime dalliance with bad sitcoms. After all, my friends were engaged with similar rituals (and their parents probably were, too); like me, they were nested in their own cool basements watching the same shows. We were unapologetic about our time in front of the television's sweet blue glow, and our parents did not shake their heads grimly about our loss of innocence, youth, or creativity. Instead, watching several hours of television at a time seemed an acceptable—even commonplace—activity, a healthy interlude from swimming, biking, and hanging out at the Ben Franklin candy aisle.

The very ordinariness of my television habit precipitated a certain kind of cultural shock when, in the mid-80s, I attended a Christian college and discovered kids who grew up *without a television*. There were parents, apparently, who thought that television would rot their children's souls, if not their minds. My new classmates' Saturday nights had been spent reading C.S. Lewis's Narnia series aloud with their families, or playing board games together. Apparently, too, these kids' parents chose more covert ways to have sex, since they had no Technicolor entertainment to distract their children. Did they slip away between turns at Monopoly and Risk?

Suddenly, I had to be very careful about the friends I chose. I knew nothing about *The Lion, the Witch, and the Wardrobe*, and couldn't imagine what we would talk about if my classmates knew the strategy for Risk, but not that Marsha Brady broke her nose right before the prom. How could I associate with people who did not put aside their studies on Thursday nights for Must See TV, who preferred finishing a philosophy paper to watching *The Cosby Show, Cheers,* and *Night Court?* Would I be able to relate to someone who could not tell me where she was when the *Fantasy Island/Love Boat* crossover show aired?

This was a cultural conflict at its finest: unacknowledged, pervasive, divisive. We were all white, middle-class Christians at our university, yet those who listed Zenith or Panasonic as a family member (and there were, in fact, a number of us) found few commonalities with the TV-less crowd. The conflict was fueled, too, by the insufferable sense of superiority enjoyed by the television abstainers. They acted as if avoiding TV was a virtue, as if they were somehow better because they preferred Lewis to *The Love Boat* and played checkers with their parents rather than hibernating in a basement while their folks made love two creaking floors above. The "Kill your Television" stickers I saw slapped on their cars provided an obvious reminder: these people felt themselves above TV, and seemed to enjoy the cache of being out of touch with the real world.

If the snobbery about TV was fueled by narrow-minded classmates' Christian self-righteousness, in graduate school, where I studied English literature, those who cast dispersions on television were motivated by something else: an academic self-righteousness, the conviction that anything associated with popular culture was well beneath the realm of their attentive minds. In graduate seminars, my peers mused loftily about deconstruction, text, post-structuralism—the names of their critical gurus scattershot through lengthy diatribes while everyone else in the class nodded enthusiastically. Who were these people? Had they been reading Derrida and Cixous on the very nights I had been vicariously cruising through Acapulco? A few of my fellow Ph.D. candidates wrote papers for popular culture conferences, but their essay titles alone suggested a purely theoretical approach to television: "Sexual Politics on the Love Boat: A Socio-Hermeneutical Reading of Julie and Dr. Bricker" or "Deconstructing Cousin Oliver: Eschatology and the Brady Bunch."

Mentioning my love for television in this environment seemed career suicide, and so I assumed the language of my peers at school, decrying the destructive rot of television, its crass humor, its appeal to the lowest common denominator. At night, after spending hours trying to understand even one word of Derrida, I tuned in to my nightly shows, to *Seinfeld* and *ER* and *Friends*, watching with curtains drawn figuratively, if not literally.

And then it happened: in a seminar on the Nineteenth Century American Epic, the professor slipped a Seinfeldian allusion ("Not that there's anything wrong with it") into his new historical interpretation of Whitman's *Leaves of Grass*. I noticed two or three smiles in the room, fissures in the mask of television-hating conceit. So there were others, after all: compatriots who had buried their love of TV for the sake of keeping up appearances.

In time, those who had smiled at the *Seinfeld* reference, who shared this darkest secret, would meet informally, covertly, to talk about our watching habits. Behind the closed doors of our cramped office space, we dissected *Frasier's* plotlines, talked about the verisimilitude of *ER's* medical traumas, considered the potential of a Rachel and Ross affair. And while our conversations were more mature—dare I say, more intellectual—than the Sunday school discussions I had with my friends two decades earlier, they were also more alike than different, sharing, as it were, a fundamental admiration for that oft-misunderstood and maligned medium.

Now well into my career as an English professor at a Christian university, I try hard to maneuver between the cultural Scylla and a Charybdis of television hatred. Conservative Christians stand on Scylla's rocky shores, pronouncing television the tool of the devil, reflective of

Hollywood's evil empire, beset with immoral programs intent on turning children into homosexuals and liberals. Colleagues, meanwhile, try to suck me into the whirlpool of their own intellectual elitism, denouncing TV as the bane of thinking society, blaming today's sitcoms for our students' inability to write, study—or, apparently—to stay awake in their classrooms.

On this, at least, conservative Christians and intellectuals seem to agree: television is bad, bad, bad.

But I don't buy it, this condemnation of a media that has always been such a good friend. For I'm reminded of my old basement's cool embrace, the familiar opening lines of *The Love Boat* theme song, and the promise of a few hours' oasis, followed—the next day—by a community of TV-believers discussing their favorite shows. And in a vast sampling of one, I cannot imagine how television has made me any shallower a scholar, or any more deficient a person of faith.

So I am starting my own children on a consistent diet of television fare, on *Spongebob* and *Dora* now, and maybe (later, much later) old *Fantasy Island* reruns on cable. Hopefully someday, my boys will also be conversant in the ways of the Bradys, et al., will know what it feels like to sprawl in front of the blue screen after a hard day's play. When that happens, I know I can safely turn on the television, grab my husband, and head upstairs.

In Memory of a Book
by Valzhyna Mort

books die

from dark bedrooms
where the only road
paved by a yellow lamp
led to their pages
they are stuffed in every corner of a house
thus turning it into a huge book cemetery.
those whose names do not ring any bell
are taken to the attic
where they lay—twenty books in one box—
a mass grave

books become widows

in empty apartments
nobody's heart beats above them
no one shares with them a dinner
or drops them into a bathtub

nobody watches them
lose their pages
like hair
like memory

books age alone

and the most sensitive book
stays there forever
in a cold bed
covering its head with a pillow
suppressing the scream of its black letters

old books
neglected graves

Millbrook, April 2006

Utopia

by Valzhyna Mort

after the sunset
our town is deserted like a train station
in its schedule
there's nothing
but the sun and the moon.

the ocean rushes at seagulls
like a dog on a leash
and the tower clock clears its throat every hour
but never dares to speak out.

and till the next dawn
lovers fix our bodies
with saliva—they oil our pores
with hands—they repair our faces.
that is why we don't look anything like each other.
because we are hand-made.

during the day the waves curl up like the locks
of blue-haired Malvina
and we brush them with our soft bodies

we welcome you to the colony of the sun
whose yellow flag—a glass of lemonade—waves over every table

the ocean massages the planet's core
and the night waits through the day in our black hair

in the afternoon our blood boils
and pours out through our nose and mouth
onto white ocean stones
turning them into red apples
and we offer those apples to our lovers
and they break their teeth against them.

this is why we know neither good nor evil.
sometimes our words can cut meat.

when we are betrayed
we go deep into the water
and watch how our heartbeat
scrambles the ocean into foam
and throws high waves on the shore
where children drown

and again the moon hangs like a white cocoon
so that at dawn a red moth would open its wings
and come down to the brook
and our men try to subdue it
they jump on its back
like overripe plums falling from trees
to tame the horse of the planet
and then with their lips dry from thirst
they rush to our mouths

and through them
they pull out our hearts
like buckets full of cold water
out of wells
and then they let it fall down with a roar.

and this is why our hearts ache.

if a heart could be pulled out like a tooth
if memory could be killed
we'd have been so happy living
under the yellow lemonade flag.

and the new day is at the town gates
like a trojan horse
that carries inside the whole army of the sun
and our men take it to the central square
their naked bodies like god's pointed finger
and our love to them is dangerous and blind
like a wasp that swarms around the house.

we eat malachite grapes
and waffles thin as a spider's web
and the sun marches through the town
wearing a triangle of birds, a napoleon's hat.

in our afternoon sleep
we are visited by a white zebra
she's praying for us

beads of black grapes are running through her fingers
and her white eyelashes are like sails bloated by the wind

sails hanging on the horizon
like fish's washed linens

when it gets dark
we put ocean shells to our ears
and listen
holding our breath
to Malvina with her head shaved bald
who weeps while picking up in the dark
blue locks of her famous hair.

Berlin 2006

Just a Huge Bullshit Session

Barrelhousing with Paul Soter of Broken Lizard

The Broken Lizard comedy troupe is a study in paradox. Five college buddies with an easygoing approach to making movies, yet the results are anything but slapdash. Despite no formal acting training or film school degrees, their movies are solidly acted and directed with, if not flourish, then panache. Five comedians who write very funny jokes, but whose comedic ethos grows organically out of their characters, whose emotions and reactions to things ring hilariously true.

But most of all, Broken Lizard is a study in group dynamics. Their movies succeed because, as friends and as collaborators, Broken Lizard succeeds. They are their own best focus group, and the results are frequently brilliant and always interesting—the comedic masterpiece *Super Troopers*, horror spoof *Club Dread*, a mostly behind-the-scenes contribution to the *Dukes of Hazzard* remake, and their most recent movie, *Beerfest*, a story of two men regaining their family honor by beating Germans at beer pong. Up next is a "prequel" to *Super Troopers*.

Quite frankly, we at *Barrelhouse* are envious. Hell, we even picked up a fifth editor so we could look more like them. So we recently had the opportunity to chat with Broken Lizard member Paul Soter, and we couldn't pass it up.

Paul is directing his first movie, *Watching the Detectives*, a film noir spoof starring Cillian Murphy (*28 Days Later* and *Batman Begins*) and Lucy Liu. He is also a new father.

Barrelhouse: From your perspective, what are some of the pleasures and perils of collaboration, as both a writer and performer?

Paul Soter: The pleasures of collaboration: Probably what's been best about it is that we've been around to support each other. We had years and years of going nowhere. I don't know that any of us would have stuck through the failure and rejection if we'd been going it alone. Or if we didn't still enjoy the hell out of the camaraderie.

Perils: We waste so much goddamn time farting around. We'll shoot the shit for the better part of two hours before we get any work done.

BH: One thing that seems cool about Broken Lizard is that you are all able to play a variety of characters: it's not like one guy is always the asshole character, the other is the ladies man, another the nerd. Is this a conscious decision, to avoid pigeonholing? Is this also true in your writing? Or does one guy always write certain roles?

PS: Yeah, some of it is to avoid pigeonholing. And also to keep it fun for us as actors. Every actor should get to play an asshole, or get the girl at least once. Actually each guy dreads being stuck with the romantic storyline. It's always the dullest part. We try to write as many drafts as possible before we internally cast a film, so that everybody is writing not knowing who he's playing. It keeps us honest, because frankly, once it's cast, everybody starts coming up with more jokes for himself. Surprise, surprise.

BH: Your comment on the writing and acting process brings up interesting questions in terms of your development as actors. Because the Broken Lizard humor often grows organically out of the character, what things are you doing and have you done to develop as actors?

PS: We are almost entirely untrained as actors. Stolhanske took a movement class once, and we nearly laughed him out of town because he went and bought Capezio shoes. Oh, no, actually Lemme and Stolhanske took an acting class at some washed-up dude's apartment back in the 90s. This guy once spent an entire hour-long session making Stolhanske repeat the line from Romeo and Juliet, "Tis torture not mercy," over and over again, poking poor Erik in the chest to try and rile him up. I think Stolhanske quit after that session. Probably Lemme too.

BH: We're still kind of curious about the process, like, how does it actually work to sit down and write a movie with a bunch of other guys? Do you meet every day? Does one of you take the lead initially, or do you do it, more or less live, as a big group? On revisions, does each take a crack at it and then all revise together? Do you sit around in a room with a few pounds of dope and a case of Boone's Farm and just not come out until you have a script ready? If so, what flavor of Boone's Farm—we prefer Kountry Kwencher, while others swear by Strawberry Hill. In addition, how do you guys deal with the inevitable conflicts that arise out of collaborating? For example, the other day two *Barrelhouse* editors couldn't agree on a submission so they "took it outside," and the rest of us just went with the decision of whoever came back in—"the Two Men Leave, One Man Enter" strategy.

PS: We get together as much as possible. When we're close to shooting something, it can be about every day. These days, guys are busy with a lot of individual projects, so now it's more like once a week. And it's very casual. We go through ideas. If there's a script, we go page by page and someone will talk about what's not working. Then we'll all bat shit around to see if we can come up with something better. We trade off project by project then have to put it all on paper. It's just a huge bullshit session. If we can't agree, we'll fight it out until someone is convinced, or a new idea comes along. Or we'll table it for a while. Start over again next draft. It can actually be the best part of the whole process, because sometimes you'll go home at the end of the day, and your stomach hurts because you just spent eight hours laughing. But some days you go home exhausted because you spent eight hours arguing whether "crap" is better than "shit," or "douchebag" is better than "dickwad." Dope is more present in the early stages, when you just want to bat around ideas and don't want to be constrained within the bounds of sobriety. No Boone's Farm, although when I read what you wrote, I thought it said "Kountry Kvetcher," which would be a funny new flavor of Manischevitz, don't you think?

BH: What was the inspiration for your new movie, *Watching the Detectives*? How was the experience different from working on a Broken Lizard movie?

PS: You know, I had some vague ideas floating around in my head, and at some point a few years ago I thought that this was a simple and small enough idea that I might be able to get the money to direct it. It's a blast working with the guys, but it's a pretty democratic process from start to finish. I wanted to see what it's like to be the King Shit and have everything get funneled through me. And you know what? It rocks.

BH: Without giving away who exactly is "watching the detectives," can you give us an overview of the main plot, characters, and the actors?

PS: Cillian Murphy is a film noir buff that gets his shit all turned upside down by Lucy Liu, who appears to almost be a character stepped down from a movie. She likes to screw with him and make him feel like he's inside a movie. He has to figure out if she's perfect for him, or going to drive him bonkers.

BH: If you had to gay marry any of the other guys in the troupe, who would it be and why?

PS: I would marry Lemme and Heffernan. I think they'd make an adorable couple and I'd be flattered if they let me do the honors.

BH: Who were the comedians that influenced you personally, and also inspired Broken Lizard as a group, to do comedy? What about them did you emulate?

PS: Always tough to answer. You know, you get to a certain age, and get turned on to comedy, and you start absorbing everything around you. Movies. TV. Stand-up. Books. So you've got five guys bringing in years and years of humor they've absorbed since childhood. I always think that it's probably easier for someone outside the group to say what we're channeling, because I just don't think we're aware of what we're trying to do, other than crack each other up. Why don't you tell me who you think we emulate?

BH: You have out-interviewed the interviewer! Well, here goes: it's not so much the "who" but rather the "vibe" that seems to be an influence on you guys. We definitely get a 70s vibe from you guys, where, in a sense, "anything goes" in terms of a relaxed comedic sensibility, but not at the cost of a well-done movie. Does this make any sense? And also, what is the comedian/movie that has had a huge influence on you, Paul Soter?

PS: Yeah, the relaxed vibe I think is a fair way to put it. "Quaalude Comedy" is how they'll come to describe us when we're dead (from Quaalude overdoses). For me, the most influential comedy would be either a Woody Allen (*Take the Money and Run/Bananas*) or Mel Brooks (*Young Frankenstein/Blazing Saddles*).

BH: What does Broken Lizard bring to the comedic table in comparison to your contemporaries, such as Ferrell, Carrel, Carrey, Wilson and Vaughan, the *South Park* guys, etc.? In other words, what is the Broken Lizard "aesthetic" as compared and contrasted to the performers mentioned above?

PS: I would guess that our most definitive quality is that collective dynamic. I think we'd all admit that none of us has the charisma of any of those guys, but we have a unique sort of group chemistry that comes from us being longtime friends. I think the people who dig us feel like they see themselves, a version of their own gang of buddies.

BH: What are the Broken Lizard troupe's goals with regards to breaking into television?

PS: I don't know that we have a place in television. We like being pretty uncensored. We've been very lucky, in that we've been given a loose leash most of the time. In our limited experience in TV, we've found that you really have a huge number of people who insist on putting their stink on material. I really don't think we'd respond well to that.

BH: Is there anything about television that you would find fulfilling creatively, if the whole "meddling" thing didn't exist?

PS: Well, some would say you can't have great television without meddling. (See *Scooby Doo*.) I think the potential for reaching a ton of people is kind of cool. Otherwise, I can't really see the upside. Maybe having a great theme song, like the one from *Family Ties*.

BH: Whatever Dane Cook's faults as a comedian, and to many of us they are legion, he was very savvy about using the Internet to build a fan base. With *Super Troopers*, you guys did something similarly innovative in terms of building up a grassroots following. Can you talk about that a little bit?

PS: I would love to say that we were savvy in how *Super Troopers* cultivated a big grassroots following, but honestly, we had nothing to do with it. I think people just passed the DVD around, told their friends about it. We're terrible self-promoters. We like going on the road, meeting people, etc. But that's about all we're good at. We go on MySpace and see that Dane Cook has over one million friends, and we say, "Of course! Let's do that!" But that involves, I think, being incredibly motivated and putting up content on a regular basis, and we've always had a hard time with that. It takes us forever to reach a consensus on the content of a movie every few years. There's no way we could agree on weekly/monthly Internet content. And yet I'm sure that'll be our downfall.

BH: You can pretty much grade out critics on how they evaluate dramas, and even learn something from them. But they seem to have no idea about what is funny. What is it about comedy that flummoxes movie critics?

PS: Yeah, it's weird. Like other genres, it's totally subjective, but there seems to be a way to intellectualize criticism of drama. Or music. But with comedy, it's strictly I Thought It Was Funny or I Didn't Think It Was Funny. You can have studied film for years and years, but it's not going to have any bearing on how you judge a comedy film. It's based entirely on your own sense of humor. I just find it asinine when a critic says a movie isn't funny. Who the fuck is you? If you've got such a dynamite sense of humor, why are you writing movie reviews for the *Daily Bugle*? I think very few critics—Roger Ebert is one of them—will say, "Look, this comedy isn't for me. It's not my style, but there are people who love this stuff." He seems to not be afraid to say how pointless his job is when it comes to judging comedy.

BH: What is your favorite Patrick Swayze movie and why?

PS: Wow. Reminds me of a good story. (My fave is *Red Dawn*, by the way.) So, Lemme is a huge Swayze fan. Years ago, when we were trying to get *Super Troopers* made, we were all crashing with a friend here in LA. We got invited to a party, and Lemme spots Swayze across the room. This is his big moment. He orchestrates an introduction. He's so ready to dazzle him. And then he totally flubs the whole thing. I think he got nervous and asked him something like, "So how was it making *Youngblood*? Was it cool?" So naturally, Swayze shook him pretty fast, but we were all psyched. So now it's like 5 a.m., and we've all gone to sleep. Heffernan wakes up to the sound of Lemme laughing across the room. He asks him what the hell he's laughing about, and Lemme says, "I just caught myself thinking of all the things I should have said to Swayze."

So you see, at the end of the day, all five of us are a bunch of dumb starfuckers.

For

Frankie

by
Paul Maliszewski

December 2, 2002

Dear President Bush,

On Sunday I suffered some confusion when I awoke from a nap and found the room already dark. My face was cupped in my left hand and for several seconds I did not know where I lay. I'd fallen asleep on the floor, in my living room, while it was light out still. Before sleeping I had thought, "There is enough time to accomplish something signifi-cant." I thought, "You only have to get up now." Then I thought, "And yet, nothing will be done." Then I thought something else, I don't re-member what. My blinking slowed, my eyes shut, and I slept.

When I awoke, the first fingers of my hand, the index and middle fingers, rested against my temple. The other two fingers, my ring finger and my pinky, shaded my mouth, covering it somewhat in the manner of a moustache and somewhat like a cap to stop any speech from issuing forth. My thumb I had tucked under my chin. My hand had cramped while I slept, and so I started to rub some life back into it. My fingers stubbornly held their positions and retained their partial outline of my face.

At first I thought I was in Houston, Texas, sir, in a house that I shared with my brother and one part of the rugby team at Sam Houston State University, in nearby Huntsville. My brother was in high school then and trying to finish. I had dropped out the year before, as soon as I was legally able, and had no plans to return. We had moved out of our mother's house—"out from under our mother," we said—because we found ourselves increasingly unable to stomach, let alone abide, her attempts to fashion, shape, and reform us into a religious family after my father died.

Or, at least, I found myself less able to take the requisite trips to church—they were daily—and the nagging that accompanied any re-fusal or excuse, however good. Nor could I tolerate the holding hands before supper and the hastily mumbled prayer, the only one any of us knew by heart: "God is great, God is good, let us thank him for our food. Amen." The prayer cast a wicked spell over me; pronouncing the words turned me into a child again, a helpless infant blowing bubbles with my saliva.

So one night I refused to say the prayer.

My mother said, "Harvey, just say the prayer."

I said, "I don't want to say your stupid prayer." I was, so you know, sir, nineteen years old at the time, almost twenty. If I said I felt just then all of nine, I'd be exaggerating.

My mother said, "Just say the prayer."

"It's a child's prayer," I said. "I'm not a child anymore."

My brother meanwhile examined his napkin as if it was a lost scrap from the Dead Sea Scrolls.

"Say it," my mother said.

"It's a baby's prayer," I said.

"No big words," my mother said. "You should have no problem."

"Oh, fuck off already," I said.

"Would you speak to your father that way?"

I was silent. I probably wouldn't speak to my father that way, but that was hardly the point.

"No," my mother said. "You'd never speak to your father that way."

"Dad wouldn't make me recite some stupid baby prayer," I said.

"Maybe if we had all spent more time praying," my mother said, "your father would still be alive today."

"Maybe there'd be world peace, too," I said.

"Harvey," my mother said, her patience with me expired long ago, "why must you be so..." She paused then, looking for the right word, searching. Her eyes, downcast, read the tabletop left to right as if every bad thing about me was written there. "Difficult," she said, finally. It wasn't the word she wanted. It wasn't even close. I hoped I was being much worse than merely difficult.

My brother looked up, ready to contribute at last. "Come on, Harvey," he said, "say the prayer."

"You say the baby prayer," I said, "baby."

My brother looked at me as if I'd just struck him. When, I wondered, did everyone become so fucking sensitive? My brother said the prayer, his face continuing to register only shock.

When he was done, my mother looked at him and smiled. "Thank you," she said.

"What I like about that prayer—" I said.

"Stop it," my mother said.

"What I really love—" I said.

"Harvey," my brother said. "Please?"

"I love how 'good' is supposed to rhyme with 'food,' but it doesn't."

"Enough," my mother said.

"They don't rhyme at all," I said. I pronounced the words again, elongating the vowels, and shook my head.

We ate our meal in silence, sir. We passed the plates and bowls and salt without exchanging a single request or word of thanks. My mother and brother avoided eye contact with me. That night I told myself a thousand times that I was right. The words bounced around my mind like a handball in an empty room: they found their way back to me, and I hurled them into the air again. I was right. I was right. I was right.

God wasn't great. I couldn't pretend otherwise. I suspect my brother could play along—he tends to be a bit of a stoic about life's unpleasant experiences, which is to say life in general—but was even then smart enough to realize that as soon as I packed my clothes and car magazines my mother would likely double her efforts to live a pious and righteous and thoroughly religious life.

So we left, basically. We moved out. The guys on the rugby team just happened to be looking for roommates. The situation they offered was not ideal. We didn't know them. They didn't care to get to know us. And they weren't great guys either.

The house was an old Victorian on a generous corner lot, a Painted Lady long unpainted and now existing somewhere between quaint dilapidation and being condemned. You could say that it stood upright, but then you could not say much more. Over the years, the parade of the house's owners and landlords had divided and subdivided its large, high-ceilinged rooms into smaller and smaller parcels of floor space, always with no thought given to logic and no consolation offered to aesthetics. Most rooms did not, just as an example, possess a single electrical outlet. Extension cords crisscrossed the floors, snaked around the corners, and ran under the doors. One forgotten hot plate, or a little space heater left on to beat back the draftiness, could short out several rooms.

The rugby players had decorated the house with various team flags. The flags featured colored bars, triangles, a one-eyed bear, a snake rising up on its tail, a wooden-staved barrel, and an eagle that looked plucked and then partially roasted. I didn't know what any of it meant. It all was as unintelligible as a foreign language and as inexplicable as a knife buried in a pillow frozen in a block of ice found in the middle of a quiet, peaceful meadow. I gathered from eavesdropping on a few of their conversations—I do eavesdrop—that some of the flags celebrated British teams. Whatever their origin or meaning, the flags adequately covered the holes in the wall that our roommates punched when their teams—British or otherwise—lost. The rugby players made a sport of breaking one another's belongings, drank heavily of a beer named for a minor Norse god, and, as late nights wore into early mornings, issued physical challenges that involved jumping off the roof, driving into mailboxes, and smashing pots and pans over their heads.

Once, they took a grocery cart and filled it up with newspapers stolen from a Boy Scout and his Cub Scout brother who were going door-to-door asking for recyclables in order to earn their conservation badges. After running the scouts off and raining empties down upon their heads, the rugby players lit the news on fire and sent the whole mess—grocery cart and newspapers—blazing down a hill and through an intersection. At that hour the streetlights flashed red along the cross street and yellow to the traffic approaching and traveling away from the hill.

My brother said, "At least the grocery cart didn't break any traffic laws."

The rugby players teetered on the narrow edge between such violence and mawkish, even tearful displays of their camaraderie, which was to last, they swore, until their deaths. My brother, finding that even stoicism had its limits, wished at least once a weekend that their deaths might arrive quickly and not without a little pain.

Even when feeling returned finally to my fingers, they still refused to obey, or even relax, and become a hand again, something to use. I held my left hand in my right and continued to try and rub the cramps away. My first two fingers pointed away from me, the second two pointed toward my right hand. My thumb pointed back at me. Did this mean something in International Sign Language? Was I stuttering over some letter? It was, at best, an ambiguous gesture: at once angry and accusatory, while remaining willing to acknowledge the right hand's complicity as well as place ample blame on me, the hand's commander, the individual with the authority to hold the hand to his face in the first place.

I slept on the floor of the house in Houston. I grew accustomed to it. I didn't have a bed. I told myself that sleeping on the floor was good for my back. I told myself that millions of people had, over the years, slept on millions of floors. And millions more people had slept on the bare earth before there were floors. I told myself all manner of lies to get through the night. A person can, I believe, grow accustomed to almost anything, and I never speak more untruthfully—am never more dishonest—than when I am speaking to myself about myself.

In a house of tiny bedrooms, my brother slept in the tiniest, in a bed my mother purchased for him. The bed touched three walls of the room. Two men delivered it one day while he was at school. The leader—for there are always leaders among delivery men, and the distinctions are clear, a bit of seniority, some gray at the temples, an intelligence, impossible to hide, behind the eyes—came to the door and said, "You Mr. Franklin Strub?"

I said, "No, Frankie's my brother."

The leader said, "We got a bed here for Franklin Strub from a"—he produced a clipboard from under his arm, flipped a page, and ran his fingers down a column of names, moving his lips as he read—"from a Mrs. Lyle Strub."

"I'm Frankie's brother," I said. "And that's my mother." I pointed down at the clipboard and waited for him to say something. "Can I accept?" I asked.

The leader checked the clipboard again and consulted some additional column. While I waited I felt as if I'd just asked if he could find it in his heart to accept me, a substitute, admittedly second rate.

"Says here the bed's for Franklin," he said. He looked at me again. There was a second of intense evaluation, time enough to make one thousand minute calculations. "But I guess you can sign for it," he added.

Had he said, "Your mother asked that you not sleep in this bed, ever, and not for a second assume it is yours, and not for a moment allow yourself to believe that she would do something kind for you," her intentions would have been communicated no less clearly to me.

In the mornings, I woke Frankie up for school. I made him sit down and have a little breakfast, usually cereal and milk, with slices of fresh fruit. I cleared away the rugby players' empties, accumulated from the night before, so that he'd have somewhere to sit and do his homework, if he had homework to do. I wiped the table down with a wet cloth so that Frankie never found it sticky. I used soap. I did my best to understand his math exercises, which hurt my head and seemed nothing like the math exercises of my own school days, behind me, thank god. I tried to make a home for Frankie, sir, an environment with just the right mixture of continuity, stability, and love. I believe I did this. If you met my mother and asked for her opinion of me and Frankie moving out, she will tell you I stole Frankie away and that I corrupted her baby. I do not believe this. I cannot. But then I have been known to lie to myself about myself.

But consider that Frankie had perfect attendance—and received the awards certificates to prove it—while he lived with me, in the house in Houston, in the tiniest bedroom, with a window that looked out onto a backyard of dirt and crabgrass and chicken wire and, in the middle of the yard, a small but growing hill of beer bottles, their brown glass occasionally appearing golden when the sunlight, just for a second or two, struck them the right way.

I slept outside Frankie's door, like his guard dog.

I developed a certain pride, or perhaps something of an anxiety or mania, about Frankie getting up in the morning, readying himself, and making it to the bus stop. At night, as I lay down on the floor and pulled my blankets around me, as I tried to get comfortable, I told myself to wake up at six. I repeated this instruction several times, until I was sure it had taken, and I was programmed. And I awoke. I always did. I never missed a morning. But still, in spite of my perfect record, I never shook the feeling, immediately upon waking, that I had overslept and, in doing so, made Frankie miss school. As a result I slept more lightly, starting at every sound, every footstep anywhere in the house.

120

Every flush of every toilet brought me up out of my dreams gasping for air, taking deep breaths of consciousness and exhaling panic. I began to wake up earlier, to utter quiet in a blackened room of a dark house. I slept less.

Yesterday I thought for sure I had overslept, that Frankie would never have time for a decent breakfast, let alone a shower. Except, of course, Frankie and I don't live in the house in Houston any longer, and haven't for years—I guess it would be fifteen years at least—and I don't sleep on the floor, generally, if I can help it, and anyway don't have anybody to wake up save myself, and Frankie, my brother, whom I have not seen in too long, I'm ashamed to say, these days calls himself Frank.

Keep up the good work, sir.

Sincerely,
Harvey Strub

Ambien

by Sarah Sloat

The moon bakes its marvelous loaf;
the body half-wakes
to break it.

Slumber has always smelled of vanilla,
yeast and semolina.
Doped up to doze,

the flesh augments; hunger
outsizes the sun
into a spectacle darkness might swallow.

The tongue mongers texture,
hand to mouth—
nutmeats crushed between teeth

or a cool sluice
of cream, smooth
as a stretch of dreamlessness.

From drug to plunder
this swoon is a short
in the circuit of urges—

feasts masquerading as sleep, lunar fuel,
the inner primitive minding the spit
when the hunt's done.

Duped by fullness, all night the sated
brain wakes and wakes
unrested, to taste weariness

like a wan braid of dough
uncoiling, while in another room,
sleep lays the table.

The Gaze

by Gary J. Whitehead

for Betsy

From the passing plane
we were just one more

wide-awake window
of the many-eyed

colossus, a yellow iris
in the million-visioned

disinterested island.
But had the most

imaginative passenger
ridden our beam of light

he might have seen
for himself that what shone

from your room
was something both old

and new, like the moon
just risen, a trajectory

traced already behind
so many other lit or unlit

windows of the planet
but no less beautiful

for having been done
before. Every pore

of skin on blue skin
a window. Our mouths

windows. Every molecule
of creation a window

and someone or something
on either side, looking.

In each issue of Barrelhouse, we ask an artist to interpret and adapt one of the stories from our website. This issue includes "Baldy," an original story by Joe Killiany, here adapted by cartoonist Gordon McAlpin.

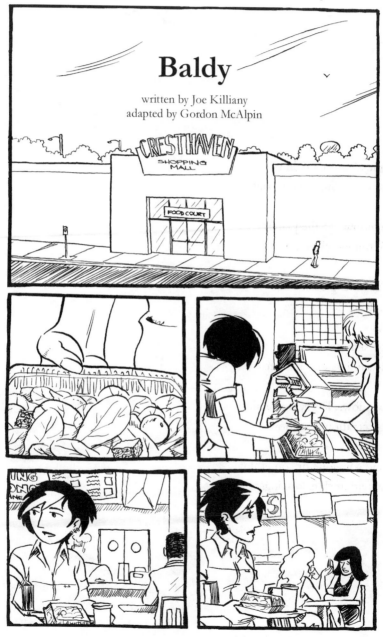

Baldy

written by Joe Killiany
adapted by Gordon McAlpin

fiction. poetry. pop flotsam. cultural jetsam.

Barrelhouse

Barrelhouse

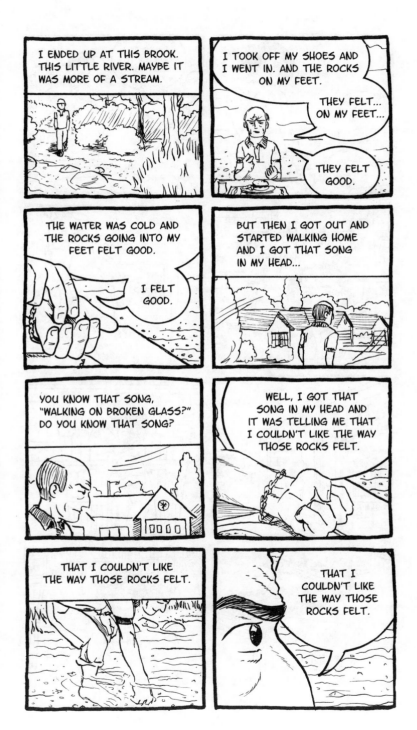

fiction. poetry. pop flotsam. cultural jetsam.

CONTRIBUTORS

Wendy Babiak writes poetry in lieu of threatening letters to government officials. She lives in Shreveport, Louisiana, with her husband and two children. Her turn-ons include environmental activism and good organic cooking; her turn-offs include closed-mindedness and religious fundamentalism, which she realizes is somewhat redundant.

David Barringer dramatizes the life of the modern suburban family in his semi-autobiographical second novel, *American Home Life,* due out summer 2007. He is the author of the novel *Johnny Red,* the fiction collection *Twisted Fun,* and the book of design criticism *American Mutt Barks in the Yard,* published in Emigre 68. Email: dlbarringer@gmail. com. Site: davidbarringer.com.

Matt Bell lives in Saginaw, Michigan with his wife, Jessica. His fiction has appeared in many literary magazines, including *Hobart, Caketrain, Juked,* and *McSweeney's Internet Tendency,* and has been nominated three times for the Pushcart Prize. He is the Reviews Editor for *SmokeLong Quarterly,* and can be found online at www.mdbell.com.

Ilana Boivie is Barrelhouse's copy editor and a graduate student in economics. She enjoys long walks on the beach, wine tasting, and cheap Mexican drugs.

Kylos Brannon makes pretty pictures. Sometimes, they move. myspace.com/badpennyfilms

Mark Peebles Brown lives in Seattle. His stories have appeared recently in *Natural Bridge, Madison Review* and *New Delta Review.*

Joan Colby has had five books of poetry published: *The Atrocity Book, The Lonely Hearts Killers, How The Sky Begins to Fall, The Boundary Waters* and *Blue Woman Dancing in the Nerve.* She has had over 800 poems in such periodicals as *Poetry, Mid American Poetry Review, The Hollins Critic, Atlanta Review, the new renaissance, Grand Street,* etc. She is the recipient of a Fellowship in Literature from the Illinois Arts Council. Previously a writer in residence for the IAC, she is currently the Editor of Illinois Racing News, a publication for the state Thoroughbred breeders organization. She lives on a small horse farm in northern Illinois with her family.

Rebecca Cook writes prose and poetry and has published in many literary journals, most recently *Northwest Review*, *Powhatan Review*, *Margie*, *Orchid*, and *Story South*. Her chapbook *The Terrible Baby* is available from Dancing Girl Press.

You can bet that **Barbara Duffey** is wearing gloves right now, though she lives in Houston, TX. Her poems have appeared in the *Indiana Review*, *Epicenter*, and the *Blue Mesa Review*, and are forthcoming in *Prairie Schooner*.

Cecelia Ferriera has often sworn to give up the brush, but to no avail. She wants to have clean fingernails and talk about the weather, but that seize to be. She creates every second she can. Her main theme is the ever so intricate human psyche and she delves too deep often. Her main gallery is on the internet. She is currently residing in Lisbon but is in the process of returning to her home country, South Africa. Europe just doesn't smell like earth. her work can be viewed at www.artwanted. com/ratinha

Charlottesville, Virginia based artist **Michael Fitts** has been using oil paint on reclaimed scrap metal for ten years. He has shown in New York, NY, Washington, D.C., Bethesda, MD, Richmond, VA and Charlottesville, VA. Fitts is represented in the Washington D.C. area by the Fraser Gallery in Bethesda, MD where he will have a solo show this coming September. His paintings can be seen at www.mfitts-art.blogspot.com.

Tod Goldberg is the author of the three books of fiction, including the novels *Living Dead Girl*, a finalist for the Los Angeles Times Book Prize, and *Fake Liar Cheat* and, most recently, the short story collection *Simplify*, a 2006 Finalist for SCBA Award for Fiction and winner of the Other Voices Short Story Collection Prize. His short fiction has appeared in numerous journals and magazines, including *Other Voices, The Sun* and the *Santa Monica Review,* twice receiving Special Mention for the Pushcart Prize. He lives in La Quinta, CA and teaches creative writing at the UCLA Extension Writers' Program.

Eva Hooker is Professor of English and Writer in Residence at Saint Mary's College, Notre Dame, Indiana. *The Winter Keeper,* a hand bound chapbook (Chapiteau Press, Montpelier, Vermont, 2000), was a finalist for the Minnesota Book Award in poetry in 2001. Her poems have recently appeared or are forthcoming in *The Harvard Review, Water-Stone, Orion, Agni* (electronic) and *The Notre Dame Review.* She is a Sister of the Holy Cross.

Amorak Huey has been a newspaper journalist for 13 years. He is currently Assistant Sports Editor at The Grand Rapids Press in Michigan. He also is completing an MFA at Western Michigan University. His poems have appeared in Lullwater Review, The Driftwood Review, Square Lake, Birmingham Arts Journal and Elysian Fields Quarterly, among other places.

Joe Killiany is one of the four founding fiction editors of Barrelhouse.

Jennifer L. Knox was born and raised in Lancaster, California, where absolutely anything can be made into a bong. Her work is featured in *Best American Poetry 2006,* and her book of poems, *A Gringo Like Me,* is available from Soft Skull Press.

Sandra Kohler's second collection of poems, *The Ceremonies of Longing,* (Pitt Poetry Series, 2003) was winner of the 2002 AWP Award Series in Poetry. Her poems have appeared in journals including *The New Republic, The Colorado Review, Prairie Schooner, The Gettyburg Review, Diner* and *Elixir* over the past twenty-eight years. After living for years in rural Central Pennsylvania she has recently moved to Boston's Dorchester neighborhood.

Kate Lovelady learned everything she knew about poetry at Northwestern University; she has since forgotten at least half. In 2005, Kate was hired as Leader of the Ethical Society of St. Louis, a community dedicated to inspiring ethical living.

Pete MacDonald's fiction has appeared in *Inkwell, Flashquake,* and a now-defunct literary magazine out of Amsterdam called *Beyond the Indus.* He works as a public defender in Seattle, where he sees lots of movies and writes the occasional non-fiction piece. He is currently rewriting the revision of the rethinking of the reworking of the twenty-sixth draft of a novel.

Paul Maliszewski's Letters to the President have appeared in *Fence, StoryQuarterly, Unsaid,* and other magazines. His writing has also been published in *Harper's, The Paris Review,* and the Pushcart Prize anthologies.

Gordon McAlpin is a digital artist for a marketing agency in Chicago, Illinois. He writes and illustrates *Multiplex* (www.multiplexcomic. com), a weekly humor webcomic about the staff of the Multiplex 10 Cinemas, as well as the irregular non-fiction webcomic *Stripped Books* (www.strippedbooks.com).

Allison McEntire is a teaching assistant at Florida State University. Her poems have appeared in *Pedestal Magazine* and the *Vanderbilt Review.*

Melanie Springer Mock is an associate professor in the Department of Writing and Literature at George Fox University, Newberg, Oregon. Her book, *Writing Peace: The Unheard Voices of Mennonite Great War Objectors,* was published by Cascadia in 2003, and her work has appeared in *Adoptive Families, The Chronicle of Higher Education,* and *Brain, Child,* among other places. She lives in Dundee, Oregon, with her husband and two boys.

Valzhyna Mort was born in 1981 in Minsk. Her new book of poetry

"Factory of Tears" will come out from Copper Canyon Press. In 2005 she received Gaude Polonia scholarship (Warsaw, Poland) and in 2006 - Literarisches Colloquium Berlin fellowship (Berlin, Germany). She lives in DC.

Jay Ryan has been making screen-printed posters in Chicago since 1995, and has worked for hundreds of "independent" bands, such as Shellac, Andrew Bird, the Melvins, Fugazi, and the Flaming Lips. His prints typically feature concerned animals, mischievous household objects, and the basic principles of physics. Jay plays bass guitar in the rock band Dianogah.

Sarah Sloat grew up in New Jersey, where she went to university. She now works for a news agency in Germany, where she's lived for the past 14 years. Among her favorite poets are Lucie Brock-Broido and Vasko Popa.

Gary J. Whitehead is the author of *The Velocity of Dust*, as well as three chapbooks of poetry. His writing awards include a New York Foundation for the Arts grant in poetry, the Pearl Hogrefe Fellowship at Iowa State University, and the PEN Northwest Margery Davis Boyden Wilderness Writing Residency Award. He teaches high school English at Tenafly High School and lives in New York.

For more Barrelhousey goodness, visit our website.
What'll you find there? We're so glad you asked.

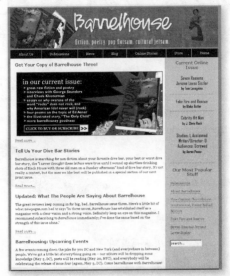

**Original
fiction,
updated
all the time**

Essays, reviews,
and the rantings
of people who
take pop culture
way too seriously

Interviews
with people
who are
way cooler
than us

**Subscription
information**

**Submission
guidelines**

**The Literary
Dodgeball
Challenge
(duck!)**

The Barrelhouse Buzz, the little
e-mail list that could...or can...or
just might, someday, if it ever got
off its ass and got its shit together

**...and more
Barrelhousey goodness.**

OKAY, SO WE JUST LIKE SAYING
"BARRELHOUSEY GOODNESS."

www.barrelhousemag.com

fiction. poetry. pop flotsam. cultural jetsam.